It's another Quality Book from CGP

This book is for anyone doing the **Edexcel Level 1/Level 2 Certificate in Biology** or the **Edexcel International GCSE in Biology**.

It gives you all the important information as clearly and concisely as possible — along with some daft bits to try and make the whole experience at least vaguely entertaining for you.

Paper 2

This book covers both Paper 1 and Paper 2 material. Some material is needed for **Paper 2 only** — we've clearly marked this in green boxes.

The Paper 2 questions in the book are also printed in green.

Paper 2

What CGP is all about

Our sole aim here at CGP is to produce the highest quality books — carefully written, immaculately presented and dangerously close to being funny.

Then we work our socks off to get them out to you — at the cheapest possible prices.

Contents

Published by CGP

From original material by Paddy Gannon.

Editors:
Ellen Bowness, Ben Fletcher, Murray Hamilton, Christopher Lindle,
Edmund Robinson, Hayley Thompson, Karen Wells.

ISBN: 978 1 84762 689 9

With thanks to Janet Cruse-Sawyer, Rosie McCurrie and Glenn Rogers for the proofreading.
With thanks to Judith Hayes for the external review.
With thanks to Anna Lupton for the copyright research.

Groovy website: www.cgpbooks.co.uk

Printed by Elanders Ltd, Newcastle upon Tyne.
Jolly bits of clipart from CorelDRAW®

Characteristics of Living Organisms

Welcome to the wonderful world of Biology. It's wonderful because it's all about you. Or at least, it's all about <u>living organisms</u> — which includes you. You may not think you have much in common with a slug or a mushroom, but you'd be wrong. You see, <u>all living organisms</u> share the same <u>eight basic characteristics</u>...

① **_They Need Nutrition_**

Living organisms need nutrients to provide them with <u>energy</u> and the <u>raw materials</u> for growth and repair. Nutrients include things like <u>proteins</u>, <u>fats</u> and <u>carbohydrates</u>, as well as <u>vitamins</u> and <u>minerals</u>. See pages 12 to 13.

② **_They Respire_**

Organisms <u>release energy</u> from their <u>food</u> by a process called respiration. See page 28.

③ **_They Excrete Their Waste_**

Waste products such as <u>carbon dioxide</u> and <u>urine</u> have to be <u>removed</u>. The removal of waste is called excretion. See page 40.

④ **_They Respond to Their Surroundings_**

Living organisms can <u>react</u> to <u>changes</u> in their <u>surroundings</u>. See page 43.

⑤ **_They Move_**

Organisms <u>move towards</u> things like <u>water</u> and <u>food</u>, and <u>away</u> from things like <u>predators</u> and <u>poisons</u>. Even plants can move a bit.

⑥ **_They Can Control Their Internal Conditions_**

Internal conditions include <u>temperature</u> and <u>water content</u>. See page 47.

⑦ **_They Reproduce_**

Organisms have to produce <u>offspring</u> (children) in order for their <u>species</u> to <u>survive</u>. See p.52-53.

⑧ **_They Grow and Develop_**

Yup, even the smallest organisms have to <u>grow</u> and <u>develop</u> into their <u>adult form</u>.

Hang on — that means Peter Pan wasn't a living organism...

Every single living thing shares these same eight characteristics. Amazing, huh? You'll be covering most of them in <u>a lot more detail</u> during the rest of your course, so if I were you, I'd commit them all to memory now.

Levels of Organisation

Living organisms are made up of <u>cells</u> — these are like <u>tiny building blocks</u>. Some organisms consist of a <u>single cell</u>. Some organisms are <u>multicellular</u> — they contain <u>lots</u> of cells, which need some form of <u>organisation</u>.

Cells Contain Organelles

<u>Organelles</u> are tiny structures <u>within</u> cells. You can only see them using a powerful <u>microscope</u>.

1) Here are some of the organelles found in a <u>typical animal cell</u>:

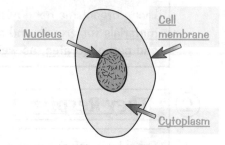

- <u>Nucleus</u>: an organelle which contains the <u>genetic material</u> that controls the cell's activities. It is surrounded by its <u>own membrane</u>.
- <u>Cell membrane</u>: this membrane forms the <u>outer surface</u> of the cell and controls the substances that go <u>in</u> and <u>out</u>.
- <u>Cytoplasm</u>: a gel-like substance where most of the cell's <u>chemical reactions</u> happen. It contains <u>enzymes</u> (see page 5) which control these reactions.

2) <u>Plant cells</u> usually have all the organelles that animal cells have, plus a <u>few extra</u>:

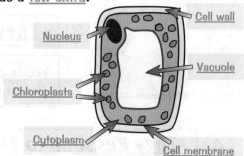

- <u>Chloroplasts</u>: <u>photosynthesis</u>, which makes <u>food</u> for the plant (see p.19), happens here. Chloroplasts contain a green substance called <u>chlorophyll</u>, which is used in photosynthesis.
- <u>Cell wall</u>: a rigid structure made of <u>cellulose</u>, which surrounds the cell membrane. It <u>supports</u> the cell and <u>strengthens</u> it.
- <u>Vacuole</u>: a large organelle that contains <u>cell sap</u> (a weak solution of sugars and salts). It helps to <u>support</u> the cell.

Cells are Specialised

1) Most cells don't look exactly like the ones shown above. They're <u>specialised</u> to carry out a <u>particular function</u>, so their structures can vary.

2) For example, in humans, <u>red blood cells</u> are specialised for carrying oxygen and <u>white blood cells</u> are specialised for defending the body against disease.

red blood cells   white blood cell

Similar Cells are Organised into Tissues

1) A <u>tissue</u> is a group of similar cells that <u>work together</u> to carry out a <u>particular function</u>.

2) For example, plants have <u>xylem tissue</u> (for transporting water and mineral salts) and <u>phloem tissue</u> (for transporting sucrose and amino acids).

3) A tissue can contain <u>more than one</u> cell type.

These tissues have a very particular function...

Tissues are Organised into Organs

1) An <u>organ</u> is a group of different <u>tissues</u> that <u>work together</u> to perform a function.

2) <u>Lungs</u> in mammals and <u>leaves</u> on plants are two examples of <u>organs</u> — they're both made up of several <u>different tissue types</u>.

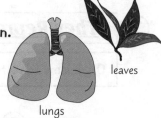

leaves

lungs

Organs Make Up Organ Systems

1) Organs work together to form <u>organ systems</u>. Each system does a <u>different job</u>.

2) For example, in mammals, the <u>digestive system</u> is made up of organs including the stomach, intestines, pancreas and liver.

Soft and quilted — the best kind of tissues...

You need to be able to <u>compare</u> the structures of <u>plant</u> and <u>animal cells</u> for the exam — so make sure you learn the features they have <u>in common</u> as well as the <u>differences</u> between them. It's thrilling stuff, I know.

Plants, Animals and Fungi

Living organisms can be arranged into groups, according to the features they have in common.
Three of these groups are plants, animals and fungi...

Learn the Features of Plants, Animals and Fungi

If you've ever wondered what features you share with a housefly,
then this table is for you. Read on to find out more...

Plants, animals and fungi have different cell structures. For more on the structure of plant and animal cells, see page 2.

Organism		Description	Examples
Plants		1) Plants are multicellular. 2) They have chloroplasts (see page 2) which means they can photosynthesise (see page 19). 3) Their cells have cell walls, which are made of cellulose. 4) Plants store carbohydrates as sucrose or starch.	Flowering plants like: • cereals (e.g. maize). • herbaceous legumes (e.g. peas and beans).
Animals		1) Animals are also multicellular. 2) They don't have chloroplasts and they can't photosynthesise. 3) Their cells don't have cell walls. 4) Most have some kind of nervous coordination (see page 43). This means that they can respond rapidly to changes in their environment. 5) They can usually move around from one place to another. 6) They often store carbohydrate in the form of glycogen.	• Mammals (e.g. humans). • Insects (e.g. houseflies and mosquitoes).
Fungi		1) Some are single-celled. 2) Others have a body called a mycelium, which is made up of hyphae (thread-like structures). The hyphae contain lots of nuclei. 3) They can't photosynthesise. 4) Their cells have cell walls made of chitin. 5) Most feed by saprotrophic nutrition — they secret extracellular enzymes into the area outside their body to dissolve their food, so they can then absorb the nutrients. 6) They can store carbohydrate as glycogen.	• Yeast — this is a single-celled fungus. • Mucor — this is multicellular and has a mycelium and hyphae.

It was hard, but I've avoided the classic 'he was a fungi to be with' joke...

OK, I'll admit it — that was a big chunk of information for you to get your head around. But if you learn the
table above, you'll know everything you need to know about plants, animals and fungi. Excellent.

Protoctists, Bacteria and Viruses

Just when you thought you'd mastered all the groups — here's a few more you need to know about...

Learn the Features of Protoctists, Bacteria and Viruses

Organism		Description	Examples
Protoctists	nucleus	1) These are single-celled and microscopic (really tiny). 2) Some have chloroplasts and are similar to plant cells. 3) Others are more like animal cells.	• Chlorella (plant-cell-like) • Amoeba (animal-cell-like) — lives in pond water.
Bacteria	cell wall, cytoplasm, circular chromosome, cell membrane, plasmids (extra bits of DNA)	1) These are also single-celled and microscopic. 2) They don't have a nucleus. 3) They have a circular chromosome of DNA. 4) Some can photosynthesise. 5) Most bacteria feed off other organisms — both living and dead.	• Lactobacillus bulgaricus — can be used to make milk go sour and turn into yoghurt. It's rod-shaped. • Pneumococcus — spherical (round) in shape.
Viruses	protein coat, DNA or RNA There's more on DNA on p.51. DNA and RNA are both nuclei acids, so they're fairly similar.	1) These are particles, rather than cells, and are smaller than bacteria. 2) They can only reproduce inside living cells. Organisms that depend on other organisms to live are called parasites. 3) They infect all types of living organisms. 4) They come in loads of different shapes and sizes. 5) They don't have a cellular structure — they have a protein coat around some genetic material (either DNA or RNA).	• Influenza virus • Tobacco mosaic virus — this makes the leaves of tobacco plants discoloured by stopping them from producing chloroplasts. • HIV

Some Organisms Are Pathogens

Pathogens are organisms that cause disease. They include some fungi, protoctists, bacteria and viruses.

E.g. **PROTOCTIST:** Plasmodium, which causes malaria.
BACTERIUM: Pneumococcus, which causes pneumonia.
VIRUSES: Influenza virus (which causes 'flu') and HIV (which causes AIDS).

Bacteria is the plural of bacterium.

I think my brother's a pathogen — he definitely causes disease...

All of the organisms on this page are really tiny — but there's just as much to know about them as the things on the previous page. So get your brain in gear and learn the table — make sure you know what a pathogen is too.

Enzymes

Enzymes Are Catalysts Produced by Living Things

1) Living things have thousands of different chemical reactions going on inside them all the time. These reactions need to be carefully controlled — to get the right amounts of substances in the cells.

2) You can usually make a reaction happen more quickly by raising the temperature. This would speed up the useful reactions but also the unwanted ones too... not good. There's also a limit to how far you can raise the temperature inside a living creature before its cells start getting damaged.

3) So... living things produce enzymes that act as biological catalysts.

> A CATALYST is a substance which INCREASES the speed of a reaction, without being CHANGED or USED UP in the reaction.

4) Enzymes reduce the need for high temperatures and we only have enzymes to speed up the useful chemical reactions in the body. These reactions are called metabolic reactions.

5) Enzymes are all proteins and all proteins are made up of chains of amino acids. These chains are folded into unique shapes, which enzymes need to do their jobs (see below).

Enzymes are Very Specific

1) Chemical reactions usually involve things either being split apart or joined together.

2) A substrate is a molecule that is changed in a reaction.

3) Every enzyme molecule has an active site — the part where a substrate joins on to the enzyme.

4) Enzymes are really picky — they usually only speed up one reaction. This is because, for an enzyme to work, a substrate has to be the correct shape to fit into the active site.

5) This is called the 'lock and key' model, because the substrate fits into the enzyme just like a key fits into a lock.

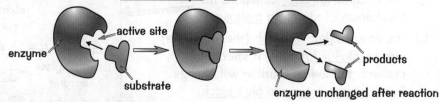

Enzymes Like it Warm but Not Too Hot

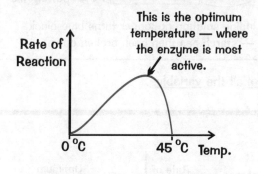

This is the optimum temperature — where the enzyme is most active.

1) Changing the temperature changes the rate of an enzyme-catalysed reaction.

2) Like with any reaction, a higher temperature increases the rate at first. This is because more heat means the enzymes and the substrate particles have more energy. This makes the enzymes and the substrate particles move about more, so they're more likely to meet up and react — they have a higher collision rate.

3) Low temperatures have the opposite effect — there's a lower collision rate and so a slower reaction.

4) If it gets too hot, some of the bonds holding the enzyme together will break.

5) This makes the enzyme lose its shape — its active site doesn't fit the shape of the substrate any more. This means it can't catalyse the reaction and the reaction stops — the enzyme can't function.

6) The enzyme is now said to be denatured. Its change in shape is irreversible (permanent).

7) Each enzyme has its own optimum temperature when the reaction goes fastest. This is the temperature just before it gets too hot and starts to denature. The optimum temperature for the most important human enzymes is about 37 °C — the same temperature as our bodies. Lucky for us.

If only enzymes could speed up revision...

Scientists have caught on to the idea that enzymes are really useful. They're used in biological detergents (to break down nasty stains) and in some baby foods (to predigest the food).

More on Enzymes

I bet you've been asked countless times how you would <u>investigate</u> the <u>effect of temperature on enzyme activity</u>. Well if you read this page, you'll finally have the answers — you're right, I am spoiling you...

You Can Investigate the Effect of Temperature on Enzyme Activity

There are a couple of different ways to investigate how temperature affects enzyme activity.

You Can Measure How Fast a Product Appears...

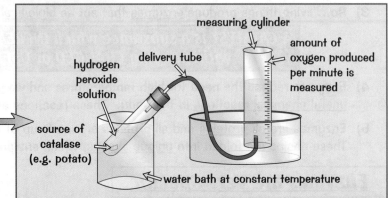

1) The enzyme <u>catalase</u> catalyses the <u>breakdown</u> of <u>hydrogen peroxide</u> into <u>water</u> and <u>oxygen</u>.

2) It's easy to <u>collect</u> the <u>oxygen</u> produced and measure <u>how much is given off in a set period of time</u>, e.g. a minute. The diagram shows you how.

3) You can run a <u>series of experiments</u>, each with the <u>water bath</u> at a <u>different temperature</u>, to see how temperature affects the <u>activity</u> of catalase.

4) Just make sure that you <u>control any variables</u> that might affect the results, e.g. enzyme concentration, pH, volume of solution, etc. This will make it a <u>fair test</u>. See page 83 for more.

...Or How Fast a Substrate Disappears

1) The enzyme <u>amylase</u> catalyses the breakdown of <u>starch</u> to <u>maltose</u>.

2) It's easy to <u>detect starch</u> (the substrate) using <u>iodine solution</u> — if starch is present, the iodine solution will change from <u>browny-orange</u> to <u>blue-black</u>.

3) You can <u>time</u> how long it takes for the starch to disappear by <u>regularly sampling</u> the starch solution, and use the times to compare rates between different tests.

4) By <u>adjusting</u> the water bath <u>temperature</u>, you can see how temperature affects the <u>activity</u> of amylase. Again, you need to make sure you <u>control</u> all the <u>variables</u>.

Time when iodine solution no longer turns blue-black is noted — starch has then been broken down.

Enzymes Also Need the Right pH

1) <u>pH</u> also affects enzymes. If it's too high or too low, the pH interferes with the <u>bonds</u> holding the enzyme together. This changes the shape of the active site and <u>denatures</u> the enzyme.

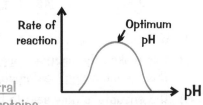

2) All enzymes have an <u>optimum pH</u> that they work best at. It's often <u>neutral pH 7</u>, but <u>not always</u> — e.g. <u>pepsin</u> is an enzyme used to break down <u>proteins</u> in the <u>stomach</u>. It works best at <u>pH 2</u>, which means it's well-suited to the <u>acidic conditions</u> there.

Mad scientists — they're experi-mental...

Everyone loves doing <u>experiments</u> — admittedly there aren't any Bunsen burners involved in the ones above, but they're a good way of seeing science in action. If you're sitting Paper 2, you also need to know about the effect of pH on enzyme activity. Which is more than enough of a reason to <u>learn</u> this page.

Diffusion

Diffusion is <u>really important</u> in living organisms — it's how a lot of <u>substances</u> get <u>in</u> and <u>out</u> of cells. Basically particles <u>move about randomly</u>, and after a bit they end up <u>evenly spaced</u>.

Don't be Put Off by the Fancy Word

1) <u>Diffusion</u> is simple. It's just the <u>gradual movement</u> of particles from places where there are <u>lots</u> of them to places where there are <u>fewer</u> of them.

2) That's all it is — just the <u>natural tendency</u> for stuff to <u>spread out</u>.

3) Here's the fancy <u>definition</u>:

> <u>Diffusion</u> is the <u>net movement</u> of <u>particles</u> from an area of <u>higher concentration</u> to an area of <u>lower concentration</u>.

4) Diffusion happens in both <u>liquids</u> and <u>gases</u> — that's because the particles in these substances are free to <u>move about</u> randomly.

5) The <u>simplest type</u> is when different <u>gases</u> diffuse through each other.
   This is what's happening when the smell of perfume diffuses through a room:

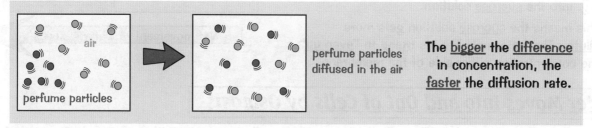

perfume particles diffused in the air

The <u>bigger</u> the <u>difference</u> in concentration, the <u>faster</u> the diffusion rate.

Cell Membranes are Pretty Clever...

1) They're clever because they <u>hold</u> the cell together <u>but</u> they let stuff <u>in and out</u> as well.

2) Substances can move in and out of cells by <u>diffusion</u>, <u>osmosis</u> (see next page) and <u>active transport</u> (see page 10).

3) Only very <u>small</u> molecules can <u>diffuse</u> through cell membranes though — things like <u>glucose</u>, <u>amino acids</u>, <u>water</u> and <u>oxygen</u>. <u>Big</u> molecules like <u>starch</u> and <u>proteins</u> can't fit through the membrane.

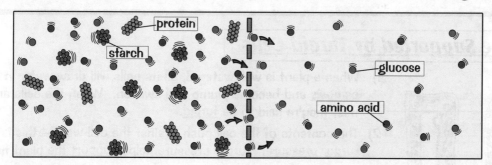

1) Just like with diffusion in air, particles flow through the cell membrane from where there's a <u>higher concentration</u> (more of them) to where there's a <u>lower concentration</u> (not such a lot of them).

2) They're only moving about <u>randomly</u> of course, so they go <u>both</u> ways — but if there are a lot <u>more</u> particles on one side of the membrane, there's a <u>net</u> (overall) movement <u>from</u> that side.

Revision by diffusion — you wish...

Wouldn't that be great — if all the ideas in this book would just gradually drift across into your mind, from an area of <u>high concentration</u> (in the book) to an area of <u>low concentration</u> (in your mind — no offence). Actually, that probably will happen if you read it again. Why don't you give it a go...

Osmosis

If you've got your head round <u>diffusion</u>, osmosis will be a <u>breeze</u>. If not, you need to read the previous page...

Osmosis is a Special Case of Diffusion, That's All

> <u>OSMOSIS</u> is the <u>net movement of water molecules</u> across a <u>partially permeable membrane</u> from a region of <u>higher water concentration</u> to a region of <u>lower water concentration</u>.

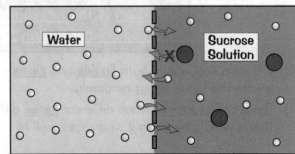

1) A <u>partially permeable</u> membrane is just one with very small holes in it. So small, in fact, only tiny <u>molecules</u> (like water) can pass through them, and bigger molecules (e.g. <u>sucrose</u>) can't. A <u>cell membrane</u> is a <u>partially permeable</u> membrane.

2) The water molecules actually pass <u>both ways</u> through the membrane during osmosis. This happens because water molecules <u>move about randomly</u> all the time.

3) But because there are <u>more</u> water molecules on one side than on the other, there's a steady <u>net flow</u> of water into the region with <u>fewer</u> water molecules, e.g. into the <u>sucrose</u> solution.

4) This means the <u>sucrose</u> solution gets more <u>dilute</u>. The water acts like it's trying to "<u>even up</u>" the concentration either side of the membrane.

Water Moves Into and Out of Cells by Osmosis

1) <u>Tissue fluid</u> surrounds the cells in the body — it's basically just <u>water</u> with <u>oxygen</u>, <u>glucose</u> and stuff dissolved in it. It's squeezed out of the <u>blood capillaries</u> to supply the cells with everything they need.

2) The tissue fluid will usually have a <u>different concentration</u> to the fluid <u>inside</u> a cell. This means that water will either move <u>into the cell</u> from the tissue fluid, or <u>out of the cell</u>, by <u>osmosis</u>.

3) If a cell is <u>short of water</u>, the solution inside it will become quite <u>concentrated</u>. This usually means the solution <u>outside</u> is more <u>dilute</u>, and so water will move <u>into</u> the cell by osmosis.

4) If a cell has <u>lots of water</u>, the solution inside it will be <u>more dilute</u>, and water will be <u>drawn out</u> of the cell and into the fluid outside by osmosis.

Plants Are Supported by Turgid Cells

Turgid Cell   Flaccid Cell

1) When a plant is well watered, all its cells will draw water in by <u>osmosis</u> and become plump and swollen. When the cells are like this, they're said to be <u>turgid</u>.

2) The contents of the cell push against the cell wall — this is called <u>turgor pressure</u>. Turgor pressure helps <u>support</u> the plant tissues.

3) If there's no water in the soil, a plant starts to <u>wilt</u> (droop). This is because the cells start to lose water and so <u>lose</u> their turgor pressure. The cells are then said to be <u>flaccid</u>.

4) The plant doesn't totally lose its shape though, because the <u>inelastic cell wall</u> keeps things in position. It just droops a bit.

Paper 2 (left margin)
Paper 2 (right margin)

Try saying osmosis backwards — it's not really fun, or even educational...

Osmosis is why it's bad to drink sea water. The high <u>salt</u> content means you end up with a much <u>lower water concentration</u> in your blood and tissue fluid than in your cells. Lots of water is sucked out of your cells by osmosis and they <u>shrivel and die</u>. So next time you're stranded at sea, remember this page...

Diffusion and Osmosis Experiments

For all you non-believers — here are a few experiments you can do to see diffusion and osmosis in action.

You Can Investigate Diffusion in a Non-Living System

Phenolphthalein is a pH indicator — it's pink in alkaline solutions and colourless in acidic solutions. You can use it to investigate diffusion in agar jelly:

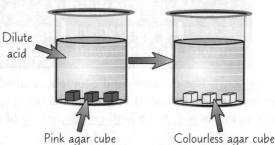

Dilute acid

Pink agar cube

Colourless agar cube

1) First, make up some agar jelly with phenolphthalein and dilute sodium hydroxide. This will make the jelly a lovely shade of pink.

2) Then fill a beaker with some dilute hydrochloric acid. Using a scalpel, cut out a few cubes from the jelly and put them in the beaker of acid.

3) If you leave the cubes for a while they'll eventually turn colourless as the acid diffuses into the agar jelly and neutralises the sodium hydroxide.

> You can investigate the rate of diffusion by using different sized cubes of agar jelly and timing how long it takes for each cube to go colourless. The cube with the largest surface area to volume ratio (see page 10) will lose its colour quickest.

You Can Investigate Osmosis in Living and Non-Living Systems

Living system — potato cylinders

Cut up an innocent potato into identical cylinders, and get some beakers with different sugar solutions in them. One should be pure water, another should be a very concentrated sugar solution. Then you can have a few others with concentrations in between. You measure the length of the cylinders, then leave a few cylinders in each beaker for half an hour or so. Then you take them out and measure their lengths again.

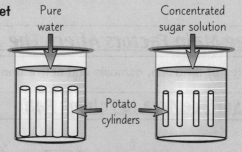

Pure water

Concentrated sugar solution

Potato cylinders

If the cylinders have drawn in water by osmosis, they'll be a bit longer. If water has been drawn out, they'll have shrunk a bit. Then you can plot a few graphs and things.

> The only thing that you should change is the concentration of the sugar solution. Everything else (e.g. the volume of solution and the time the experiment runs for) must be kept the same in each case or the experiment won't be a fair test.

Non-living system — Visking tubing

Tie a piece of wire around one end of some Visking tubing and put a glass tube in the other end — fix the tubing around it with wire. Then pour some sugar solution down the glass tube into the Visking tubing.

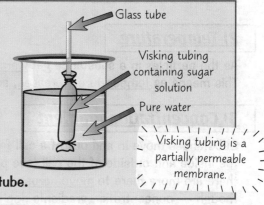

Glass tube

Visking tubing containing sugar solution

Pure water

> Visking tubing is a partially permeable membrane.

Put the Visking tubing in a beaker of pure water — measure where the sugar solution comes up to on the glass tube.

Leave the tubing overnight, then measure where the liquid is in the glass tube. Water should be drawn into the Visking tubing by osmosis and this will force the liquid up the glass tube.

Jelly, potatoes and Visking tubing — all the makings of a good night in...

OK, they weren't the most exciting experiments in the world — but make sure you know how to do them.

Active Transport

The movement of substances has been too <u>passive</u> for my liking. Put the spandex on — it's time to get <u>active</u>.

Active Transport <u>is the</u> <u>Opposite</u> <u>of Diffusion</u>

Here's what you <u>need to know</u>:

> <u>ACTIVE TRANSPORT</u> is the <u>movement of particles</u> against a concentration gradient (i.e. from an area of <u>lower concentration</u> to an area of <u>higher concentration</u>) <u>using energy</u> released during respiration.

<u>Active transport</u>, like diffusion and osmosis, is used to <u>move substances in and out of cells</u>. For example, active transport is used in the <u>digestive system</u> when there is a <u>low concentration</u> of nutrients in the <u>gut</u>, but a <u>high concentration</u> of nutrients in the <u>blood</u>:

1) When there's <u>a higher concentration</u> of nutrients in the gut they <u>diffuse naturally</u> into the blood.

2) <u>BUT</u> — sometimes there's a <u>lower concentration</u> of nutrients in the gut than there is in the blood.

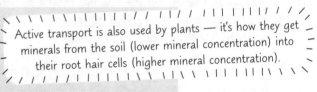
Active transport is also used by plants — it's how they get minerals from the soil (lower mineral concentration) into their root hair cells (higher mineral concentration).

3) This means that the <u>concentration gradient</u> is the wrong way. The nutrients should go <u>the other way</u> if they followed the rules of diffusion.

4) The answer is that <u>active transport</u> is responsible.

5) Active transport allows nutrients to be taken into the blood, despite the fact that the <u>concentration gradient</u> is the wrong way. This is essential to stop us starving. But active transport needs <u>ENERGY</u> from <u>respiration</u> to make it work.

diffusion   active transport

Three Main Factors <u>Affect The</u> Movement <u>of Substances</u>

The <u>rates</u> of diffusion, osmosis and active transport <u>vary</u> — they're affected by these <u>three factors</u>:

1) Surface Area to Volume Ratio

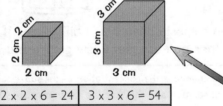

Surface area (cm^2)	2 x 2 x 6 = 24	3 x 3 x 6 = 54
Volume (cm^3)	2 x 2 x 2 = 8	3 x 3 x 3 = 27
Surface area to volume ratio	24 : 8 = <u>3 : 1</u>	54 : 27 = <u>2 : 1</u>

This can be a bit <u>tricky</u> to get your head around, but it's easier if you think of cells as <u>cubes</u> for now.

The <u>rate</u> of diffusion, osmosis and active transport is <u>higher</u> in cells (or cubes) with a <u>larger surface area to volume ratio</u>.

The <u>smaller</u> cube has a <u>larger</u> surface area to volume ratio — this means <u>substances</u> would <u>move</u> into and out of this cube <u>faster</u>.

2) Temperature

As the particles in a substance get <u>warmer</u> they have <u>more energy</u> — so they <u>move faster</u>. This means as <u>temperature increases</u>, substances move in and out of cells <u>faster</u>.

3) Concentration gradient

Substances move in and out of a cell <u>faster</u> if there's a <u>big difference in concentration</u> between the inside and outside of the cell (see page 7). If there are <u>lots more</u> particles on one side, there are more there to <u>move across</u>. This <u>only</u> increases the rate of <u>diffusion</u> and <u>osmosis</u> though — concentration gradients <u>don't affect</u> the rate of <u>active transport</u>.

If you're bored, work out the surface area to volume ratio of a loved one...

That's just about it for this section — all that's left for you to do is <u>actively transport yourself</u> to the next page...

Revision Summary for Section 1

Yep, it's already time to see how much you know — this is the sort of revision guide that means business. But if you're still in a state of shock from opening the book and revising for the first time, don't be worried. Do your best to answer the following questions and if you get any wrong, just flick back to the stuff that's not quite sunk in yet — then learn it until you remember it.

1) What are the eight basic characteristics that all living organisms share?

2) Name three organelles that are found in both animal and plant cells.

3) Name two organelles that are only found in plant cells. Describe their functions.

4) What is a tissue?

5) What is an organ? And an organ system?

6) What are plant cell walls made of?

7) How do most animals store carbohydrate?

8) Give two examples of fungi.

9) Explain what is meant by the term 'saprotrophic nutrition'.

10) Give two examples of protoctists.

11) Give three features of viruses.

12) What are pathogens? Name two pathogens.

13) What name is given to biological catalysts?

14) What is a catalyst?

15) An enzyme with an optimum temperature of 37 °C is heated to 60 °C. Suggest what will happen to it.

16) Briefly describe an experiment to show how temperature can affect enzyme activity.

17) The graph on the right shows how the rate of an enzyme-catalysed reaction depends on pH:

a)* State the optimum pH of the enzyme.

b) State what happens to the relative reaction rate at the extremes of pH.

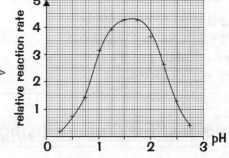

18) What is diffusion?

19) What is osmosis?

20) A solution of pure water is separated from a concentrated sugar solution by a partially permeable membrane. In which direction will molecules flow, and what substance will these molecules be?

21) Why are turgid cells important to plants?

22) Describe an experiment using a non-living system that shows diffusion taking place. Then, as a treat, do the same for osmosis.

23) How is active transport different from diffusion in terms of:

a) energy requirements,

b) concentration gradients?

24) Describe how surface area to volume ratio affects the movement of substances in and out of cells.

* Answers on p.92

Section 1 — Structures and Functions in Living Organisms

Biological Molecules

Biological molecules are things like <u>carbohydrates</u>, <u>lipids</u> and <u>proteins</u>. They're generally <u>long</u>, <u>complex molecules</u> made up from <u>smaller basic units</u>. And, unsurprisingly, they're what this page is all about...

You Need to Know the <u>Structure</u> of <u>Carbohydrates</u>, <u>Lipids</u> and <u>Proteins</u>

Carbohydrates <u>are Made Up of</u> <u>Simple Sugars</u>

- <u>Carbohydrate</u> molecules contain the elements <u>carbon</u>, <u>hydrogen</u> and <u>oxygen</u>.
- <u>Starch</u> and <u>glycogen</u> are <u>large</u>, <u>complex carbohydrates</u>, which are made up of many <u>smaller units</u> (e.g. <u>glucose</u> or <u>maltose</u> molecules) joined together in a <u>long chain</u>.

Maltose   and other simple sugars, e.g. glucose → Starch

Proteins <u>are Made Up of</u> <u>Amino Acids</u>

- <u>Proteins</u> are made up of <u>long chains</u> of <u>amino acids</u>.
- They all contain <u>carbon</u>, <u>nitrogen</u>, <u>hydrogen</u> and <u>oxygen</u> atoms.

Amino acids → Proteins

Lipids <u>are Made Up of</u> <u>Fatty Acids</u> and <u>Glycerol</u>

- <u>Lipids</u> (fats and oils) are built from <u>fatty acids</u> and <u>glycerol</u>.
- Lipids contain <u>carbon</u>, <u>hydrogen</u> and <u>oxygen</u> atoms.

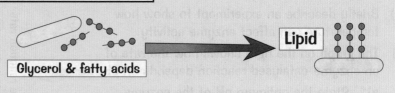

Glycerol & fatty acids → Lipid

You Can Test for <u>Glucose</u> Using <u>Benedict's Reagent</u>

1) If <u>glucose</u> is present in a sample, the <u>Benedict's test</u> will spot it.
2) You add <u>Benedict's reagent</u> (which is <u>blue</u>) to a sample and <u>heat</u> it. Make sure the solution <u>doesn't boil</u>. If the test's <u>positive</u> it will form a <u>coloured precipitate</u> (solid particles suspended in the solution).

> Always use an <u>excess</u> of Benedict's reagent — this makes sure that <u>all</u> the glucose reacts.

The <u>colour</u> of the <u>precipitate</u> changes from: blue → green → yellow → orange → brick red

3) The higher the concentration of glucose, the further the colour change goes — you can use this to <u>compare</u> the amount of glucose in different solutions.

> Benedict's test
> Time allowed: 10 mins
> _____
> Q1: Do you contain glucose?
> ☐ Yes   ☐ No
> _____
> END OF QUESTIONS

Use the <u>Iodine Test</u> for <u>Starch</u>

Just add <u>iodine solution</u> to the test sample.
- If starch <u>is present</u>, the sample changes from <u>browny-orange</u> to a dark, <u>blue-black</u> colour.
- If there's <u>no starch</u>, it stays browny-orange.

> Iodine solution is iodine dissolved in potassium iodide solution.

The Anger Test — annoy the test subject. If it goes red, anger is present...

OK, so this stuff isn't thrilling but learning it's better than being dissolved in a <u>giant vat</u> of vinegar. I mean, that's got to <u>sting</u>. And it would take an exceptionally long time. Yep, death by vinegar would be boring <u>and</u> painful.

A Balanced Diet

Your body needs the right fuel or it won't work properly — that means cutting down on the lard, I'm afraid...

You Need to Eat Different Foods to Get Different Nutrients

Nutrient		Found in...	Function(s)
Carbohydrates		Pasta, rice, sugar	Provide energy.
Lipids (fats and oils)		Butter, oily fish	Provide energy, act as an energy store and provide insulation.
Proteins		Meat, fish	Needed for growth and repair of tissue, and to provide energy in emergencies.
Vitamins	A	Liver (yum...)	Helps to improve vision and keep your skin and hair healthy.
	C	Oranges	Needed to prevent scurvy.
	D	Eggs	Needed for calcium absorption.
Mineral ions	Calcium	Milk, cheese	Needed to make bones and teeth.
	Iron	Red meat	Needed to make haemoglobin for healthy blood.
Water		Food and drink	Just about every bodily function relies on water — we need a constant supply to replace water lost through urinating, breathing and sweating.
Dietary fibre		Wholemeal bread	Aids the movement of food through the gut.

Vitamin D is also made by your body when your skin is exposed to sunlight.

A Balanced Diet Supplies All Your Essential Nutrients

1) A balanced diet gives you all the essential nutrients you need — in the right proportions.
2) The six essential nutrients are carbohydrates, proteins, lipids, vitamins, minerals and water.
3) You also need fibre (to keep the gut in good working order).

Energy Requirements Vary in Different People

You get energy from the food you eat, but the amount of energy you need isn't a set thing — it's different for everyone. The energy a person needs depends on things like...

Activity level ⟶ Active people need more energy than people who sit about all day. Bit of an obvious one, really...

Age ⟶ Children and teenagers need more energy than older people — they need energy to grow and they're generally more active.

Pregnancy ⟶ Pregnant women need more energy than other women — they've got to provide the energy their babies need to develop.

I'll have a plate of protein and carbohydrates, ta — easy on the vitamin A...

Unfortunately, revising food isn't quite as much fun as shovelling it down your gullet. But it's something you've got to do — learn all about the nutrients needed for a balanced diet, then you can treat yourself to a nice biscuit.

Energy from Food

I bet you've been told many a time not to play with your food. Well for this page I'm going to encourage you to do it, and play with fire, too. Actually it's a pretty fun experiment...

Food Can be Burnt to See How Much Energy it Contains

The posh name for this is calorimetry. You need to know how to do it with a simple experiment:

First You Need a Dry Food, Water and a Flame...

1) You need a food that'll burn easily — something that's dry, e.g. peanuts or pasta, will work best.

2) Weigh a small amount of the food and then skewer it on a mounted needle.

3) Next, add 25 cm³ of water to a boiling tube (held with a clamp) — this will be used to measure the amount of heat energy that's released when the food is burnt.

4) Measure the temperature of the water, then set fire to the food using a Bunsen burner flame. Make sure the Bunsen isn't near the water or your results might be a bit wonky.

5) Time for the exciting bit — immediately hold the burning food under the boiling tube until it goes out. Then relight the food and hold it under the tube — keep doing this until the food won't catch fire again.

6) The last thing to do is measure the temperature of the water again. Then you're ready for a bit of maths...

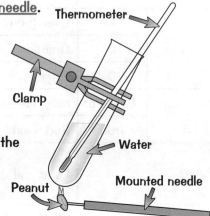

Thermometer

Clamp

Water

Peanut

Mounted needle

...Then You Can Calculate the Amount of Energy in the Food

(1) Calculate the Amount of Energy in Joules

$$\text{ENERGY IN FOOD (in J)} = \text{MASS OF WATER (in g)} \times \text{TEMPERATURE CHANGE OF WATER (in °C)} \times 4.2$$

1) 1 cm³ of water is the same as 1 g of water.

2) The 4.2 in the formula is the amount of energy (in Joules) needed to raise the temperature of 1 g of water by 1 °C.

This is the specific heat capacity of water, otherwise known as a calorie.

(2) Calculate the Amount of Energy in Joules per Gram

$$\text{ENERGY PER GRAM OF FOOD (in J/g)} = \frac{\text{ENERGY IN FOOD (in J)}}{\text{MASS OF FOOD (in g)}}$$

You need to do this calculation so you can compare the energy values of different foods fairly.

The Accuracy of the Experiment Can be Increased

1) The experiment isn't perfect — quite a bit of the energy released from burning is lost to the surroundings. It's why the energy value on the packet of the food you used is likely to be much higher than your own.

2) Insulating the boiling tube, e.g. with foil, would minimise heat loss and keep more energy in the water — making your results more accurate.

Try selling the water from this experiment as a budget energy drink...

Food scientists use calorimeters to measure food energy. They're well insulated and sealed to minimise heat loss.

Enzymes and Digestion

Various enzymes are used in <u>digestion</u> — they're produced by specialised cells and then <u>released</u> into the <u>gut</u>.

Digestive Enzymes Break Down Big Molecules into Smaller Ones

1) <u>Starch</u>, <u>proteins</u> and <u>fats</u> are <u>BIG molecules</u>. They're <u>too big</u> to pass through the <u>walls</u> of the digestive system. They're also <u>insoluble</u>.

2) <u>Sugars</u>, <u>amino acids</u>, <u>glycerol</u> and <u>fatty acids</u> are much smaller molecules. They're <u>soluble</u> and can <u>pass easily</u> through the walls of the digestive system.

3) The <u>digestive enzymes</u> break down the BIG molecules into the smaller ones.

Amylase Converts Starch into Maltose...

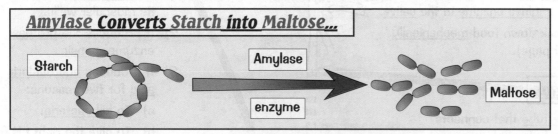

Starch — Amylase enzyme → Maltose

...and Maltase Converts Maltose into Glucose

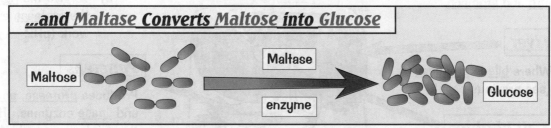

Maltose — Maltase enzyme → Glucose

Proteases Convert Proteins into Amino Acids

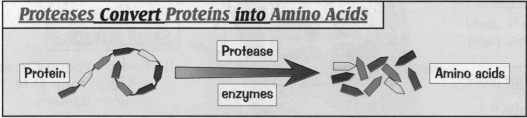

Protein — Protease enzymes → Amino acids

Lipases Convert Lipids into Glycerol and Fatty Acids

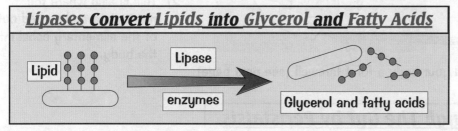

Lipid — Lipase enzymes → Glycerol and fatty acids

Bile Neutralises the Stomach Acid and Emulsifies Fats

1) Bile is <u>produced</u> in the <u>liver</u>. It's <u>stored</u> in the <u>gall bladder</u> before it's <u>released</u> into the <u>small intestine</u> (see next page).

2) The <u>hydrochloric acid</u> in the stomach makes the pH <u>too acidic</u> for enzymes in the small intestine to work properly. Bile is <u>alkaline</u> — it <u>neutralises</u> the acid and makes conditions <u>alkaline</u>. The enzymes in the small intestine <u>work best</u> in these alkaline conditions.

3) Bile also <u>emulsifies</u> fats. In other words it breaks the fat into <u>tiny droplets</u>. This gives a much <u>bigger surface area</u> of fat for the enzyme lipase to work on — which makes its digestion <u>faster</u>.

What do you call an acid that's eaten all the pies...

This all happens inside our digestive system, but there are some microorganisms (like fungi, see p.3) which secrete their digestive enzymes <u>outside their body</u> onto their food. The food's digested, then the microorganism absorbs the nutrients. Nice. I wouldn't like to empty the contents of my stomach onto my plate before eating it.

The Alimentary Canal

So, now you know what the enzymes do, here's a nice <u>big picture</u> of the <u>whole</u> of your gut.

Your Alimentary Canal Runs Through Your Body

The alimentary canal is just another name for the <u>gut</u>. You need to know the <u>names</u> and <u>functions</u> of its <u>main parts</u>, plus a few of the organs associated with it:

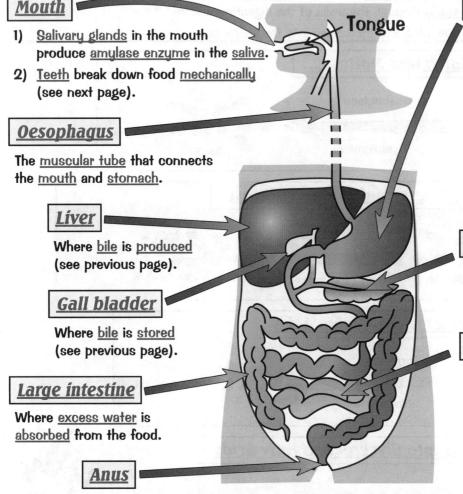

Mouth

1) <u>Salivary glands</u> in the mouth produce <u>amylase enzyme</u> in the <u>saliva</u>.
2) <u>Teeth</u> break down food <u>mechanically</u> (see next page).

Oesophagus

The <u>muscular tube</u> that connects the <u>mouth</u> and <u>stomach</u>.

Liver

Where <u>bile</u> is <u>produced</u> (see previous page).

Gall bladder

Where <u>bile</u> is <u>stored</u> (see previous page).

Large intestine

Where <u>excess water</u> is <u>absorbed</u> from the food.

Anus

Where <u>faeces</u> bid your body a fond farewell (see next page).

Tongue

Stomach

1) It <u>pummels</u> the food with its muscular walls.
2) It produces the <u>protease</u> enzyme, <u>pepsin</u>.
3) It produces <u>hydrochloric acid</u> for two reasons:
   a) To <u>kill bacteria</u>.
   b) To give the <u>right pH</u> for the <u>protease</u> enzyme to work (pH2 — <u>acidic</u>).

Pancreas

Produces <u>protease</u>, <u>amylase</u> and <u>lipase</u> enzymes. It releases these into the <u>small intestine</u>.

Small intestine

1) Produces <u>protease</u>, <u>amylase</u> and <u>lipase</u> enzymes to complete digestion.
2) This is also where the nutrients are <u>absorbed</u> out of the alimentary canal into the body.

Food is Moved Through The Gut by Peristalsis

1) There's <u>muscular</u> tissue all the way down the alimentary canal.
2) Its job is to <u>squeeze</u> balls of food (called boluses) through your gut — <u>otherwise</u> it would get <u>clogged up</u> with bits of old food. Mmm.
3) This squeezing action, which is <u>waves</u> of <u>circular muscle</u> <u>contractions</u>, is called <u>peristalsis</u>.

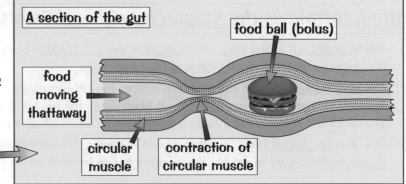

A section of the gut

food ball (bolus)

food moving thattaway

circular muscle

contraction of circular muscle

You don't have to bust a gut to revise this page...

This stuff is pretty easy to digest — learn the <u>big diagram</u> (don't worry, you won't have to draw it out) and then make sure you know what the deal is with <u>peristalsis</u>. Job done — but there's more fun on the next page...

The Digestive Process

One more page on all things <u>digestion-related</u> — get all this learnt and you'll have finished the section...

There are Five Main Stages of Digestion

The different <u>stages</u> of digestion happen in the following <u>order</u>:

1) Ingestion

This one is pretty simple — it's putting <u>food</u> (or drink) <u>into your mouth</u>.

2) Digestion

After you've ingested something, you need to <u>digest</u> it. Digestion is the <u>break-down</u> of <u>large</u>, <u>insoluble</u> <u>molecules</u> into <u>small</u>, <u>soluble molecules</u>. Your body has <u>mechanical</u> and <u>chemical</u> ways to digest food:

Mechanical	Chemical
<u>Teeth</u> and <u>stomach muscles</u>	<u>Enzymes</u> and <u>bile</u> (see page 15)

3) Absorption

If all those digested bits just <u>sat</u> in your alimentary canal, it <u>wouldn't</u> be much use. <u>Absorption</u> is the process of <u>moving molecules</u> through the <u>walls</u> of the <u>intestines</u> into the blood. <u>Digested food molecules</u> are absorbed in the <u>small intestine</u> — <u>water</u> is mainly absorbed in the <u>large intestine</u>.

4) Assimilation

You will be assimilated. Resistance is futile.

When digested molecules have been absorbed, they're <u>moved into body cells</u>. The digested molecules then become <u>part</u> of the cells — this process is known as <u>assimilation</u>. For example, when <u>amino acids</u> (from digested proteins) are assimilated, they're used by cells to make <u>cellular proteins</u>.

5) Egestion

Not everything that you ingest can be digested. All of the <u>undigested stuff</u> forms <u>faeces</u>, which are of <u>no use</u> to your body — you <u>get rid of them</u> via a one-way ticket through the <u>anus</u>. This is known as <u>egestion</u>.

Villi in the Small Intestine Help with Absorption

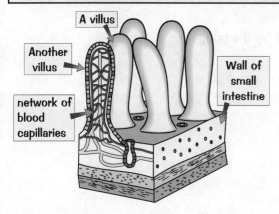

A villus

Another villus

network of blood capillaries

Wall of small intestine

1) The <u>small intestine</u> is <u>adapted</u> for absorption of food.
2) It's very <u>long</u>, so there's time to break down and absorb <u>all</u> the food before it reaches the end.
3) There's a really <u>big surface area</u> for absorption, because the walls of the small intestine are covered in <u>millions and millions</u> of tiny little projections called <u>villi</u>.
4) Each <u>cell</u> on the surface of a villus also has its own <u>microvilli</u> — little projections that increase the surface area even more.
5) Villi have a <u>single permeable</u> layer of surface cells and a very <u>good blood supply</u> to assist <u>quick absorption</u>.

Ingest this info, digest and absorb it, then assimilate it into your brain...

Now you know all the <u>fancy terms</u> for what happens to the stuff you eat (sorry, <u>ingest</u>) and all about <u>villi</u> — they look a bit weird, but they're perfect for <u>absorbing</u> digested food. If you're still wondering about the <u>assimilation</u> graphic, maybe you should take a break from revision and catch up on a certain <u>sci-fi programme</u>...

Revision Summary for Section 2

By reading this page you are hereby accepting the challenge I have created for you below. The rules are as follows: attempt to answer a question — if you get it right, move on to the next one. Get it wrong and you must shake your fist at the sky before flicking back to the page that covers the topic. Answer all of the questions correctly and you'll have completed the challenge — your prize awaits you on the next page...

1) Name the three main chemical elements that are found in carbohydrates.

2) What type of biological molecules are made up of:

   a) fatty acids and glycerol?

   b) amino acids?

3) Describe how you could use Benedict's reagent to test for glucose.

4) What could you use to see if there's starch in a sample?

5) Why does the body need proteins? What foods contain proteins?

6) What nutrients does the body get energy from?

7) Eric has just been to see his doctor. He has been told that he needs to increase the amount of vitamin D in his diet. What foods can Eric get this nutrient from? Why does Eric need vitamin D?

8) Explain fully what is meant by the term 'a balanced diet'.

9) Explain the difference in energy requirements between:

   a) children and older people.

   b) a woman who's pregnant and one who isn't.

10) a) Describe a simple experiment to measure the amount of energy in a food.

    b) Give one way you could make the experiment more accurate.

11) What is the main role of digestive enzymes?

12) Name the enzymes that convert starch into glucose.

13) What do proteases do?

14) When lipids are digested, what molecules are they broken down into?

15) Where in the body is bile:

    a) produced?   b) stored?   c) used?

16) What are the two functions of bile?

17) Describe the function(s) of the:

    a) mouth,

    b) oesophagus,

    c) small intestine,

    d) pancreas.

18) Describe the process of peristalsis. Why is peristalsis needed by the body?

19) What is the difference between ingestion and egestion?

20) Put the following digestive processes in order that they occur:

    a) absorption

    b) assimilation

    c) digestion

21) Explain how villi help with absorption in the small intestine.

Photosynthesis

Plants can make their own food — it's ace. Here's how...

Photosynthesis Produces Glucose Using Sunlight

1) Photosynthesis is the process that produces 'food' in plants. The 'food' it produces is glucose.

2) Photosynthesis happens in the leaves of all green plants — this is largely what the leaves are for.

3) Photosynthesis happens inside the chloroplasts, which are found in leaf cells and in other green parts of a plant. Chloroplasts contain a pigment called chlorophyll, which absorbs sunlight and uses its energy to convert carbon dioxide and water into glucose. Oxygen is also produced.

You need to learn the word and symbol equations for photosynthesis:

$$\text{carbon dioxide} + \text{water} \xrightarrow[\text{chlorophyll}]{\text{SUNLIGHT}} \text{glucose} + \text{oxygen}$$
$$6CO_2 \qquad 6H_2O \qquad\qquad C_6H_{12}O_6 \qquad 6O_2$$

4) Photosynthesis is an important process because it converts light energy to chemical energy, which is stored in the glucose. This chemical energy is released when glucose is broken down during respiration (see page 28).

Leaves are Designed for Making Food by Photosynthesis

The whole structure of leaves is geared towards that. You need to know all the different parts of a typical leaf shown on the diagram:

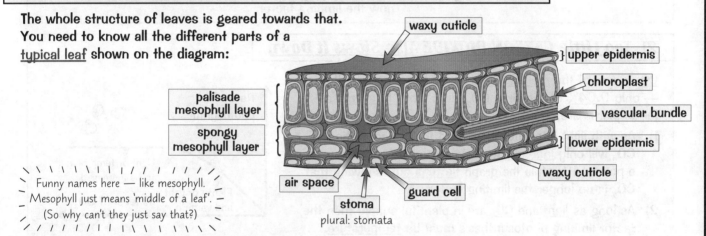

waxy cuticle

upper epidermis

chloroplast

vascular bundle

lower epidermis

waxy cuticle

palisade mesophyll layer

spongy mesophyll layer

air space

guard cell

stoma
plural: stomata

Funny names here — like mesophyll. Mesophyll just means 'middle of a leaf'. (So why can't they just say that?)

Leaves are Adapted for Efficient Photosynthesis

1) Leaves are broad, so there's a large surface area exposed to light.

2) Most of the chloroplasts are found in the palisade layer. This is so that they're near the top of the leaf where they can get the most light.

3) The upper epidermis is transparent so that light can pass through it to the palisade layer.

4) Leaves have a network of vascular bundles — these are the transport vessels xylem and phloem (see page 24). They deliver water and other nutrients to every part of the leaf and take away the glucose produced by photosynthesis. They also help to support the leaf structure.

5) The waxy cuticle helps to reduce water loss by evaporation.

6) The adaptations of leaves for efficient gas exchange (see page 30) also make photosynthesis more efficient. E.g. the lower surface is full of little holes called stomata, which let CO_2 diffuse directly into the leaf.

I'm working on sunshine — woah oh...

Plants are pretty crucial in ensuring the flow of energy through nature. They're able to use the Sun's energy to make glucose — the energy source which humans and animals need for respiration.

Rate of Photosynthesis

A plant's rate of photosynthesis is affected by the amount of <u>light</u>, the amount of <u>CO$_2$</u>, and the <u>temperature</u> of its surroundings. Photosynthesis slows down or stops if the conditions aren't right.

The Limiting Factor Depends on the Conditions

1) A limiting factor is something which <u>stops photosynthesis from happening any faster</u>. Light intensity, CO$_2$ concentration and temperature can all be the limiting factor.

2) The limiting factor depends on the <u>environmental conditions</u>. E.g. in <u>winter</u> low temperatures might be the limiting factor. At <u>night</u>, light is likely to be the limiting factor.

There are Three Important Graphs for Rate of Photosynthesis

1) Not Enough LIGHT Slows Down the Rate of Photosynthesis

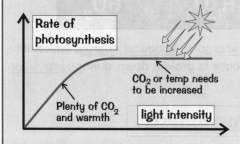

<u>Chlorophyll</u> uses <u>light energy</u> to perform photosynthesis. It can only do it as quickly as the light energy is arriving.

1) If the <u>light intensity</u> is increased, the rate of photosynthesis will <u>increase steadily</u>, but only up to a <u>certain point</u>.

2) Beyond that, it won't make any <u>difference</u> because then it'll be either the <u>temperature</u> or the <u>CO$_2$</u> level which is now the limiting factor.

2) Too Little CARBON DIOXIDE Also Slows It Down

<u>CO$_2$</u> is one of the <u>raw materials</u> needed for photosynthesis — only <u>0.04%</u> of the air is CO$_2$, so it's <u>pretty scarce</u> as far as plants are concerned.

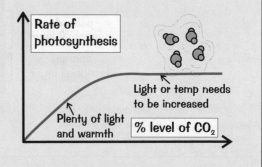

1) As with light intensity, increasing the concentration of CO$_2$ will only <u>increase</u> the rate of photosynthesis up to a point. After this the graph <u>flattens out</u>, showing that CO$_2$ is no longer the limiting factor.

2) As long as <u>light</u> and <u>CO$_2$</u> are in plentiful supply then the factor limiting photosynthesis must be <u>temperature</u>.

3) The TEMPERATURE Has to be Just Right

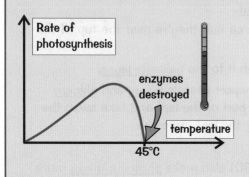

Temperature affects the rate of photosynthesis — because it affects the <u>enzymes</u> involved.

1) As the <u>temperature increases</u>, so does the <u>rate</u> of photosynthesis — up to a point.

2) If the temperature is <u>too high</u> (over about 45 °C), the plant's <u>enzymes</u> will be <u>denatured</u> (destroyed), so the rate of photosynthesis rapidly decreases.

3) <u>Usually</u> though, if the temperature is the <u>limiting factor</u> it's because it's too low, and things need <u>warming up a bit</u>.

Amount of sleep is usually my limiting factor...

So. You can create the <u>optimum conditions</u> for photosynthesis if you keep the <u>three limiting factors</u> in balance, which means plenty of <u>light</u> and <u>CO$_2$</u>, and nice, <u>warm temperatures</u> (but not too hot). You can control all three factors in a glasshouse. This'll give your plants a real boost and help you to grow some monstrous tomatoes.

Photosynthesis Experiments

The <u>two products</u> from photosynthesis are <u>glucose</u> and <u>oxygen</u> (see page 19). Glucose is stored by plants as <u>starch</u>. You can test for starch (see below) and oxygen (see next page) to <u>investigate photosynthesis</u>.

You Need to Know How to *Test a Leaf* for *Starch*

1) First, the leaf needs to be <u>killed</u> by dunking it in <u>boiling water</u> (hold it with tweezers or forceps) — this sounds a bit harsh, but it <u>stops</u> any <u>chemical reactions</u> happening inside the leaf.

2) Next, put the leaf in a boiling tube with some <u>ethanol</u> and heat the tube in a water bath. This gets rid of any <u>chlorophyll</u> that's inside the leaf. The leaf should end up a pale, <u>white-ish</u> colour.

3) Finally, <u>rinse</u> the leaf in <u>cold water</u> and add a few drops of <u>iodine solution</u> to it (see page 12). If <u>starch</u> is <u>present</u> inside the leaf, it will turn <u>blue-black</u>.

The *Starch Test* Shows Whether *Photosynthesis is Taking Place*

If a plant can't <u>photosynthesise</u>, it can't make <u>starch</u>. You can use this principle to show that <u>chlorophyll</u> and <u>CO_2</u> are <u>needed for photosynthesis</u>. Here's how...

Chlorophyll

You can show that <u>chlorophyll</u> is needed for photosynthesis using <u>variegated</u> (green and white) <u>leaves</u>. Only the <u>green parts</u> of the leaf contain <u>chlorophyll</u>.

1) Take a variegated leaf from a plant that's been <u>exposed to light</u> for a bit. Make sure you <u>record</u> which bits are <u>green</u> and which bits <u>aren't</u>.

2) Test the leaf for starch as above — you'll see that only the bits that were <u>green</u> turn <u>blue-black</u>.

3) This suggests that only the parts of the leaf that <u>contained chlorophyll</u> are able to <u>photosynthesise</u> and <u>produce starch</u>.

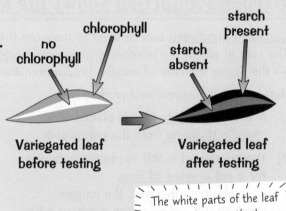

no chlorophyll | chlorophyll | starch absent | starch present

Variegated leaf before testing → Variegated leaf after testing

> The white parts of the leaf go brown because the brown iodine solution stains them.

> For both of these tests, it's important that any variables that could affect the results, e.g. the temperature, are controlled.

CO_2

1) You can show that <u>CO_2</u> is needed for photosynthesis with the apparatus shown on the right.

2) The soda lime will <u>absorb CO_2</u> out of the air in the jar.

3) If you leave the plant in the jar for a while and then <u>test</u> a leaf for starch, it <u>won't</u> turn blue-black.

4) This shows that <u>no starch</u> has been made in the leaf, which means that <u>CO_2 is needed</u> for photosynthesis.

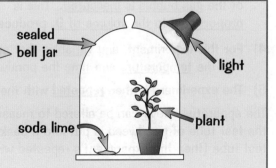

sealed bell jar | light | plant | soda lime

Some like it hot — apparently plant leaves don't...

Mass boiling of plant leaves is required here. It kind of gives you a <u>snapshot</u> of what's going on <u>inside the leaf</u> as it stops all the <u>chemical reactions</u> that are taking place. Then you're free to do some lovely <u>starch testing</u>. Admit it, you're excited... You're not? Well don't tell the plant that you nicked all the leaves for these tests from them...

More Photosynthesis Experiments

More starch testing on this page I'm afraid. But there's also a bit about how oxygen production can show the rate of photosynthesis. Don't say I don't mix things up a bit for you...

The Starch Test Shows Whether Photosynthesis is Taking Place

Remember, if a plant can't photosynthesise, it can't make starch. You can use this principle to show that light is needed for photosynthesis. Here's how:

1) To show that light is needed for photosynthesis you need a plant that's been grown without any light, e.g. in a cupboard.

2) Cut a leaf from the plant and test it for starch using iodine solution (see previous page) — the leaf won't turn blue-black.

3) This shows that light is needed for photosynthesis, as no starch has been made.

Even though the plant is kept in the dark, you need to make sure it's warm enough to photosynthesise and that there's plenty of CO_2 — or it won't be a fair test.

Oxygen Production Shows the Rate of Photosynthesis

Canadian pondweed can be used to measure the effect of light intensity on the rate of photosynthesis. The rate at which the pondweed produces oxygen corresponds to the rate at which it's photosynthesising — the faster the rate of oxygen production, the faster the rate of photosynthesis.

Here's how the experiment works:

1) A source of white light is placed at a specific distance from the pondweed.

2) The pondweed is left to photosynthesise for a set amount of time.
As it photosynthesises, the oxygen released will collect in the capillary tube.

3) At the end of the experiment, the syringe is used to draw the gas bubble in the tube up alongside a ruler and the length of the gas bubble is measured. This is proportional to the volume of O_2 produced.

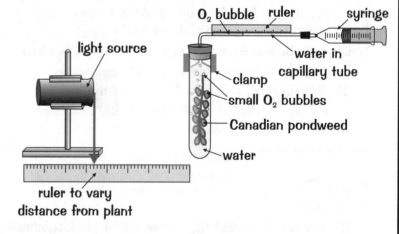

light source

ruler to vary distance from plant

O_2 bubble — ruler — syringe
water in capillary tube
clamp
small O_2 bubbles
Canadian pondweed
water

4) For this experiment, any variables that could affect the results should be controlled, e.g. the temperature and time the pondweed is left to photosynthesise.

5) The experiment is then repeated with the light source placed at different distances from the pondweed.

The apparatus above can be altered to measure the effect of temperature and CO_2 on photosynthesis, e.g. the test tube of pondweed is put into a beaker of water at a set temperature and CO_2 is bubbled into the test tube (then the experiment's repeated with different temperatures of water / concentrations of CO_2).

Canadian pondweed, eh — the British stuff probably feels a bit left out...

Poor old plant in the dark... I think the pondweed gets a much better deal, floating around in a nice, clean test tube. Anyway, the main points here are that plants in the dark won't produce any starch and that you can use pondweed to investigate oxygen production from a photosynthesising plant. Cool.

Minerals for Healthy Growth

Plants are important in food chains and nutrient cycles because they can take minerals from the soil and energy from the Sun and turn it into food. And then, after all that hard work, we eat them — it seems a little unfair, but that's the way of the world. Anyway, learn this page — it's important for healthy brain growth.

Plants Need Three Main Mineral Ions For Growth

1) Plants need certain elements so they can produce important compounds.

2) They get these elements from mineral ions in the soil.

3) If there aren't enough of these mineral ions in the soil, plants suffer deficiency symptoms.

1) Nitrates

Contain nitrogen for making amino acids and proteins.
These are needed for cell growth. If a plant can't get enough nitrates it will be stunted and will have yellow older leaves.

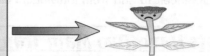

2) Phosphates

Contain phosphorus for making DNA and cell membranes and they're needed for respiration and growth. Plants without enough phosphate have poor root growth and purple older leaves.

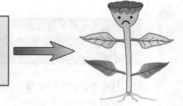

3) Potassium

To help the enzymes needed for photosynthesis and respiration. If there's not enough potassium in the soil, plants have poor flower and fruit growth and discoloured leaves.

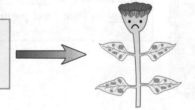

Magnesium is Also Needed in Small Amounts

1) The three main mineral ions are needed in fairly large amounts, but there are other elements which are needed in much smaller amounts.

2) Magnesium is one of the most significant as it's required for making chlorophyll (needed for photosynthesis).

3) Plants without enough magnesium have yellow leaves.

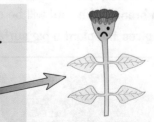

Symptoms of revision deficiency include nagging parents and poor grades...

When a farmer or a gardener buys fertiliser, that's pretty much what he or she is buying — nitrates, phosphates and potassium. A fertiliser's NPK label tells you the relative proportions of nitrogen (N), phosphorus (P) and potassium (K) it contains, so you can choose the right one for your plants and soil. Don't forget about magnesium, though — it's dead important that plants get a little bit of this, so that they can make chlorophyll.

Transport in Plants

You might be surprised to learn that there aren't tiny trucks that transport substances around plants. Then again, you might not be — either way, you need to learn the stuff on this page...

Multicellular Organisms Need Transport Systems

1) The cells in all living organisms need a variety of substances to live, e.g. plant cells need things like water, minerals and sugars. They also need to get rid of waste substances.

2) In unicellular organisms, these substances can diffuse directly into and out of the cell across the cell membrane. The diffusion rate is quick because of the short distances substances have to travel.

3) But in multicellular organisms (like animals and plants) direct diffusion from the outer surface would be too slow — that's because substances would have to travel large distances to reach every single cell.

4) So multicellular organisms need transport systems to move substances to and from individual cells quickly.

However, carbon dioxide diffuses into plants at the leaves (where it's needed).

Plants Have Two Main Transport Systems

Plants have two systems transporting stuff around. Both go to every part of the plant, but they're totally separate.

Water and minerals

Xylem tubes transport water and minerals:

The xylem carry water and mineral salts from the roots up the shoot to the leaves in the transpiration stream (see next page).

Paper 2

Phloem tubes transport food:

1) The phloem transport sugars, like sucrose, and amino acids from where they're made in the leaves to other parts of the plant.

2) This movement of food substances around the plant is known as translocation.

Paper 2

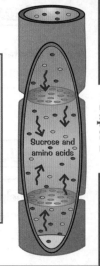

Sucrose and amino acids

Root Hairs Take In Water

1) The cells on plant roots grow into long 'hairs' which stick out into the soil.

2) Each branch of a root will be covered in millions of these microscopic hairs.

3) This gives the plant a big surface area for absorbing water from the soil.

Root hair cells also take in minerals — this is done by active transport (see page 10).

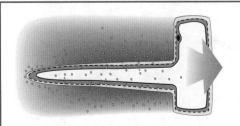

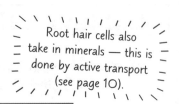

Water is taken in by osmosis (see page 8).

There's usually a higher concentration of water in the soil than there is inside the plant, so the water is drawn into the root hair cell by osmosis.

Don't let revision stress you out — just go with the phloem...

You probably did that really dull experiment at school where you stick a piece of celery in a beaker of water with red food colouring in it. Then you stare at it for half an hour, and once the time is up, hey presto, the red has reached the top of the celery. That's because it travelled there in the xylem. Isn't science amazing...

Transpiration

If you don't water a house plant for a few days it starts to go <u>all droopy</u>. Then it <u>dies</u>, and the people from the Society for the Protection of Plants come round and have you <u>arrested</u>. Plants need water.

Transpiration *is the* Loss of Water *from the Plant*

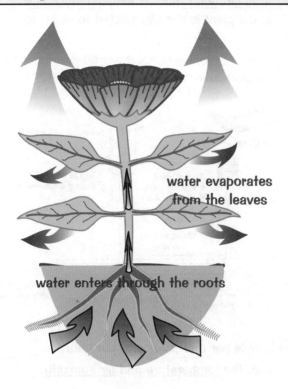

water evaporates
from the leaves

water enters through the roots

1) Transpiration is caused by the <u>evaporation</u> and <u>diffusion</u> (see page 7) of water from a plant's surface. Most transpiration happens at the <u>leaves</u>.

2) This evaporation creates a slight <u>shortage</u> of water in the leaf, and so more water is drawn up from the rest of the plant through the <u>xylem vessels</u> (see previous page) to replace it.

3) This in turn means more water is drawn up from the <u>roots</u>, and so there's a constant <u>transpiration stream</u> of water through the plant.

Transpiration is just a <u>side-effect</u> of the way leaves are adapted for <u>photosynthesis</u>. They have to have <u>stomata</u> in them so that gases can be exchanged easily (see page 30). Because there's more water <u>inside</u> the plant than in the <u>air outside</u>, the water escapes from the leaves through the stomata by diffusion.

Transpiration Rate *is Affected by* Four Main Things

1) <u>LIGHT INTENSITY</u> — the <u>brighter</u> the light, the <u>greater</u> the transpiration rate.

   <u>Stomata</u> begin to <u>close</u> as it gets darker. Photosynthesis can't happen in the dark, so they don't need to be open to let CO_2 in. When the stomata are closed, very little water can escape.

2) <u>TEMPERATURE</u> — the <u>warmer</u> it is, the <u>faster</u> transpiration happens.

   When it's warm the water particles have <u>more energy</u> to evaporate and diffuse out of the stomata.

3) <u>WIND SPEED</u> — the <u>higher</u> the wind speed around a leaf, the <u>greater</u> the transpiration rate.

   If wind speed around a leaf is <u>low</u>, the water vapour just <u>surrounds the leaf</u> and doesn't move away. This means there's a <u>high concentration</u> of water particles outside the leaf as well as inside it, so <u>diffusion</u> doesn't happen as quickly. If it's windy, the water vapour is <u>swept away</u>, maintaining a <u>low concentration</u> of water in the air outside the leaf. Diffusion then happens quickly, from an area of high concentration to an area of low concentration.

4) <u>HUMIDITY</u> — the <u>drier</u> the air around a leaf, the <u>faster</u> transpiration happens.

   This is like what happens with air movement. If the air is <u>humid</u> there's a lot of water in it already, so there's not much of a <u>difference</u> between the inside and the outside of the leaf. Diffusion happens <u>fastest</u> if there's a <u>really high concentration</u> in one place, and a <u>really low concentration</u> in the other.

Transpiration — the plant version of perspiration...

One good way to remember those <u>four factors</u> that affect the rate of transpiration is to think about drying washing. Then you'll realise there are far more boring things you could be doing than revision, and you'll try harder. No, only joking — it's the same stuff: <u>sunny</u>, <u>warm</u>, <u>windy</u> and <u>dry</u>.

Measuring Transpiration

It's time for another experiment — you get to use a piece of equipment you've probably never heard of...

A Potometer can be Used to Estimate Transpiration Rate

A potometer is a special piece of apparatus used to estimate transpiration rates. It actually measures water uptake by a plant, but it's assumed that water uptake by the plant is directly related to water loss by the leaves (transpiration). Here's how to use a potometer:

1) Cut a shoot underwater to prevent air from entering the xylem. Cut it at a slant to increase the surface area available for water uptake.

2) Assemble the potometer in water and insert the shoot under water, so no air can enter.

3) Remove the apparatus from the water but keep the end of the capillary tube submerged in a beaker of water.

4) Check that the apparatus is watertight and airtight.

5) Dry the leaves, allow time for the shoot to acclimatise and then shut the tap.

6) Remove the end of the capillary tube from the beaker of water until one air bubble has formed, then put the end of the tube back into the water.

7) Record the starting position of the air bubble.

8) Start a stopwatch and record the distance moved by the bubble per unit time, e.g. per hour.

9) Keep the conditions constant throughout the experiment, e.g. the temperature and air humidity.

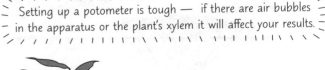

Setting up a potometer is tough — if there are air bubbles in the apparatus or the plant's xylem it will affect your results.

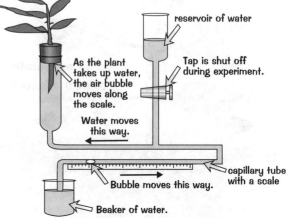

reservoir of water

As the plant takes up water, the air bubble moves along the scale.

Tap is shut off during experiment.

Water moves this way.

Bubble moves this way.

capillary tube with a scale

Beaker of water.

You Can See How Environmental Conditions Affect Transpiration Rates

You can use a potometer to estimate how different factors affect the transpiration rate. The set up above will be your control — you can vary an environmental condition (see below), run the experiment again and compare the results to the control to see how the change affected the transpiration rate.

Light intensity

You could use a lamp to increase the intensity of light that hits the plant — this should increase the transpiration rate. To decrease the light intensity, put the potometer in a cupboard (this should decrease the transpiration rate).

Temperature

You could increase or decrease the temperature by putting the potometer in a room that's warmer or colder than where did you the control experiment. An increase in temperature should increase the transpiration rate and a decrease in temperature should lower it.

Humidity

You could increase the humidity of the air around the plant by spraying a little water into a clear plastic bag before sealing it around the plant. This should decrease the rate of transpiration.

Wind speed

You could use a fan to increase the wind speed around the plant — this should increase the transpiration rate.

Potometer — I thought it might measure if something was a pot or not...

The tricky bit is setting up the apparatus — keeping air out and water in is harder than it sounds, but if you're only writing about the experiment in an exam, you don't have to worry about that. Phew. End of section three.

Revision Summary for Section 3

Congratulations. You've successfully navigated your way through another section and come through it in one piece (hopefully). If you've come through in several pieces, then I'm very concerned (but a bit curious) about your method of reading this book... Anyway, it's now time to see if, during your journey through the loveliness of section three, you actually absorbed the stuff on the pages. Have a bash at the questions below and cement this section in your brain (no actual cement is required for this).

1) Write down the word and balanced symbol equations for photosynthesis.
2) How does being broad help a leaf to photosynthesise?
3) Describe one other way that leaves are adapted for efficient photosynthesis.
4)* The graph shows how the rate of photosynthesis in plants is affected by increasing the level of carbon dioxide. Look at the graph and answer the two questions below.

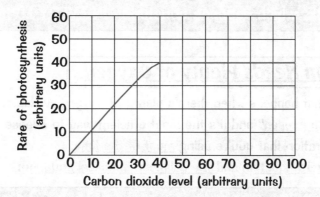

  a) At what level of carbon dioxide is the plant's rate of photosynthesis limited by another factor?
  b) Suggest two possible limiting factors on the plant's rate of photosynthesis above this level.
5) Briefly describe an experiment to show that chlorophyll is required for photosynthesis.
6) Describe an experiment that you could carry out to see how light intensity affects the rate of photosynthesis.
7) Name the three main mineral ions plants need for healthy growth.
8) How can you tell by looking at a plant that it isn't getting enough magnesium?
9) Which mineral ion is needed by plants to make chlorophyll?
10) Explain why plants and animals need transport systems to move substances around their bodies but unicellular organisms don't.
11) What is the function of xylem vessels in plants?
12) What is the function of phloem vessels in plants?
13) How does water get into a plant through its root hair cells?
14) What is transpiration?
15) How is the transpiration rate affected by: a) increased temperature, b) increased humidity?
16) Describe an experiment that you could do to measure how temperature affects the transpiration rate of a plant.

* Answers on p.92

Section 3 — Plant Nutrition and Transport

Respiration

You need energy to keep your body going. Energy comes from food, and it's released by respiration.

Respiration is NOT "Breathing In and Out"

1) Respiration is NOT breathing in and breathing out, as you might think.
2) Respiration actually goes on in every cell in your body.
3) It's the process of releasing energy from glucose.
4) Energy is released as chemical energy and heat.
5) There are two types of respiration, aerobic and anaerobic.

The chemical energy is used to do things like create large molecules from smaller ones (e.g. proteins from amino acids) and contract muscles. The heat energy helps to maintain a steady body temperature.

> RESPIRATION is the process of RELEASING ENERGY from GLUCOSE, which happens constantly IN EVERY LIVING CELL.

Aerobic Respiration Needs Plenty of Oxygen

1) Aerobic respiration is what happens when there's plenty of oxygen available.
2) Aerobic just means "with oxygen" and it's the most efficient way to release energy from glucose.
3) This is the type of respiration that you're using most of the time.
   You need to learn the word equation and the balanced chemical equation:

$$\text{Glucose} + \text{Oxygen} \longrightarrow \text{Carbon dioxide} + \text{Water} (+ \text{ENERGY})$$
$$C_6H_{12}O_6 + 6O_2 \longrightarrow 6CO_2 + 6H_2O (+ \text{ENERGY})$$

This is the reverse of the photosynthesis equation (see page 19).

Anaerobic Respiration Doesn't Use Oxygen At All

1) When you do really vigorous exercise your body can't supply enough oxygen to your muscles for aerobic respiration — even though your heart rate and breathing rate increase as much as they can. Your muscles have to start respiring anaerobically as well.
2) Anaerobic just means "without oxygen". It's NOT the best way to convert glucose into energy because it releases much less energy than aerobic respiration. In anaerobic respiration, the glucose is only partially broken down, and lactic acid is also produced.
3) The lactic acid builds up in the muscles — it gets painful and leads to cramp.
   You need to learn the word equation for anaerobic respiration in animals:

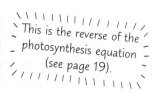

$$\text{Glucose} \longrightarrow \text{Lactic Acid} (+ \text{ENERGY})$$

Anaerobic Respiration in Plants is Slightly Different

Plants can respire without oxygen too, but they produce ethanol (alcohol) and CO_2 instead of lactic acid.
You need to learn the word equation for anaerobic respiration in plants:

Fungi like yeast also do anaerobic respiration like this — people use yeast to produce beer (see page 77).

$$\text{Glucose} \longrightarrow \text{Ethanol} + \text{Carbon Dioxide} (+ \text{ENERGY})$$

I reckon aerobics classes should be called anaerobics instead...

OK, so when you're just sitting about, you use aerobic respiration to get all your energy — but when you do strenuous exercise, you can't get enough oxygen to your muscles, so you use anaerobic respiration too.

Investigating Respiration

Still not convinced about <u>carbon dioxide</u> and <u>heat</u> being produced by <u>respiration</u>?
Well here's how to <u>detect</u> them yourself. Don't eat all the <u>beans</u>...

Carbon Dioxide Production can be Detected using an Indicator

1) You can use <u>hydrogen-carbonate solution</u> to show that living organisms produce <u>CO_2</u> as they respire.
2) Normally this solution is <u>orange</u>, but it <u>changes colour</u> to a <u>lovely yellow</u> in the presence of <u>carbon dioxide</u>.
3) Here's how you can set up an experiment to demonstrate <u>carbon dioxide production</u> by some <u>beans</u>:

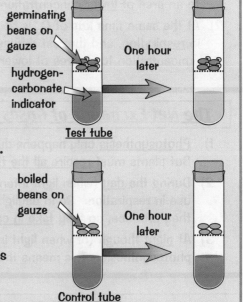

First, <u>soak</u> some <u>dried beans</u> in <u>water</u> for a day or two.
They will start to <u>germinate</u> (you should see little sprouts coming out of them). Germinating beans will <u>respire</u>.

<u>Boil</u> a <u>similar-sized</u>, second bunch of dried beans.
This will <u>kill the beans</u> and make sure they <u>can't respire</u>.
The dead beans will act as your <u>control</u>.

Now, set up the experiment as shown on the right:

- Put some <u>hydrogen-carbonate indicator</u> into two <u>test tubes</u>.
- Place a <u>platform</u> made of <u>gauze</u> into each test tube and place the beans on this.
- <u>Seal</u> the test tubes with a <u>rubber bung</u>.
- Leave the apparatus for a <u>set period</u> of <u>time</u> (e.g. an hour).
- During that time the CO_2 produced by the germinating beans should have had an effect on the <u>hydrogen-carbonate indicator</u> — it will have turned <u>yellow</u>.

4) You could also carry out this experiment with <u>small organisms</u> like woodlice or maggots (the control for these would be glass beads though).

The Heat Produced by Respiration can be Measured

On the previous page I said that <u>respiration</u> gives off <u>heat</u> (that's why <u>running</u> makes you get <u>hot</u>) — well here's an experiment to <u>measure</u> that heat. You'll be glad to know it uses more <u>dried beans</u>.

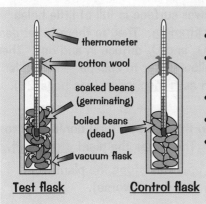

- Firstly, prepare <u>two sets of beans</u> as described in the experiment above.
- Add each set of beans to a <u>vacuum flask</u>, making sure there's some <u>air</u> left in the flasks (so the beans can <u>respire aerobically</u>).
- Place a <u>thermometer</u> into each flask and seal the top with <u>cotton wool</u>.
- Record the <u>temperature</u> of each flask daily for a week.
- The beans are well-insulated in the flasks, so when the germinating beans <u>respire</u> and produce <u>heat</u>, the <u>test flask's temperature</u> will <u>increase</u> compared to the control flask.

My results are dodgy — maybe using baked beans wasn't the best idea...

I know, not very funny, but I wasn't inspired. Try <u>drawing the diagrams</u> above to get the experiments in your head. After you've done that, you could try something fun, like trying to stick your toe in your ear...

Gas Exchange — Flowering Plants

Now's a good time to flick back to page 7 and make sure that you thoroughly know about diffusion.

Plants Exchange Gases By Diffusion

When plants photosynthesise they use up CO_2 from the atmosphere and produce O_2 as a waste product. When plants respire they use up O_2 and produce CO_2 as a waste product. So there are lots of gases moving to and fro in plants, and this movement happens by diffusion. For example:

1) When the plant is photosynthesising it uses up lots of CO_2, so there's hardly any inside the leaf. Luckily this makes more CO_2 move into the leaf by diffusion (from an area of higher concentration to an area of lower concentration).

2) At the same time lots of O_2 is being made as a waste product of photosynthesis. Some is used in respiration, and the rest diffuses out through the stomata (moving from an area of higher concentration to an area of lower concentration).

The Net Exchange of Gases Depends on Light Intensity

1) Photosynthesis only happens during the day (i.e. when there's light available). But plants must respire all the time, day and night, to get the energy they need to live.

2) During the day (when light intensity is high) plants make more oxygen by photosynthesis than they use in respiration. So in daylight, they release oxygen. They also use up more carbon dioxide than they produce, so they take in carbon dioxide.

3) At night though (or when light intensity is low) plants only respire — there's not enough light for photosynthesis. This means they take in oxygen and release carbon dioxide — just like us.

Paper 2

Leaves are Adapted for Efficient Gas Exchange

1) Leaves are broad, so there's a large surface area for diffusion.

2) They're also thin, which means gases only have to travel a short distance to reach the cells where they're needed.

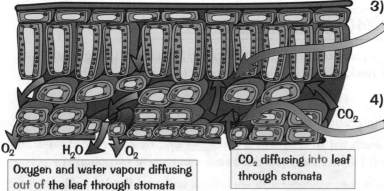

O₂   H₂O   O₂

Oxygen and water vapour diffusing out of the leaf through stomata

CO_2

CO_2 diffusing into leaf through stomata

3) There are air spaces inside the leaf. This lets gases like carbon dioxide and oxygen move easily between cells. It also increases the surface area for gas exchange.

4) The lower surface is full of little holes called stomata. They're there to let gases like CO_2 and O_2 diffuse in and out. They also allow water to escape — which is known as transpiration (see page 25).

5) Stomata begin to close as it gets dark. Photosynthesis can't happen in the dark, so they don't need to be open to let CO_2 in. When the stomata are closed, water can't escape. This stops the plant drying out.

6) Stomata also close when supplies of water from the roots start to dry up. This stops the plant from photosynthesising (bad), but if they didn't close, the plant might dry out and die (worse).

7) The opening and closing of stomata is controlled by the cells that surround them (called guard cells).

I say stomaaaarta, you say stomaaaayta...

Here's an interesting fact — a biggish tree loses around 1000 litres of water from its leaves every day. That's about as much water as the average person drinks in a whole year, so the roots have to draw lots of water from the soil to replace it. No wonder the stomata close when the soil's dry or when it's too dark to photosynthesise.

Gas Exchange — Flowering Plants

Like the sprinter who forgot to tie his shoes, the experiments are coming thick and fast now. Here's one to measure gas exchange in plants — if you skipped the previous page, I'd go back and read it if I were you.

Hydrogen-carbonate Indicator Shows Changes in CO_2 Concentration...

1) You might remember from p.29 that a solution of hydrogen-carbonate indicator in air with a normal CO_2 concentration is orange.

2) Well if the CO_2 concentration of the air increases, more CO_2 will dissolve in it, and it becomes more yellow.

3) And if the CO_2 concentration of the air decreases, CO_2 will come out of the solution, and it becomes purple.

...So You Can Use it to Show Differences in Net Gas Exchange in Plants

Here's an experiment to show how light affects gas exchange:

1) Add the same volume of hydrogen-carbonate indicator to four boiling tubes.

2) Put similar-sized, healthy-looking leaves into three of the tubes and seal with a rubber bung. Trap the leaf stem with the bung to stop it falling down into the solution if you need to. Keep the fourth tube empty as a control.

3) Completely wrap one tube in aluminium foil, and a second tube in gauze.

4) Place all the tubes in bright light. This will let plenty of light on to the uncovered leaf, and a little light onto the leaf covered in gauze. The leaf covered in foil will get no light — assuming you've wrapped it up properly.

5) Leave the tubes for an hour, then check the colour of the indicator.

And The Results are in...

1) There shouldn't be any change in the colour of the control tube.

2) You'd expect the indicator in the darkened tube to go yellow. Respiration will still take place but there will be no photosynthesis, so the CO_2 concentration in the tube will increase.

3) You'd expect the indicator in the shaded tube to stay a similar colour. With a little photosynthesis and some respiration taking place, roughly equal amounts of CO_2 will be taken up and produced by the leaf, so the CO_2 concentration in the tube won't change very much.

4) You'd expect the indicator in the well-lit tube to go purple. There will be some respiration, but lots of photosynthesis, leading to net uptake of CO_2 by the leaf. This will lower the CO_2 concentration in the tube.

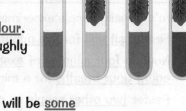

I'll swap you 10 litres of carbon dioxide for 5 litres of methane...

This experiment might sound like the most long-winded way possible to get some different-coloured tubes, but CO_2 is pretty hard to measure (being colourless, odourless and generally like the rest of the air doesn't help), so this is actually a pretty neat way to show it. Plus you can watch an episode of your favourite TV program, or do a whole lesson on gas exchange while it's doing its thing. So give it a go, then draw a nice colour picture of it.

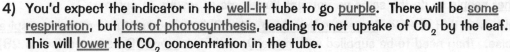

The Respiratory System and Ventilation

You need to get <u>oxygen</u> into your bloodstream to supply your cells for <u>respiration</u>. You also need to get rid of <u>carbon dioxide</u> from your blood. This all happens in your <u>lungs</u> when you breathe air <u>in and out</u>.

The Lungs Are in the Thorax

1) The <u>thorax</u> is the top part of your body.

2) It's separated from the lower part of the body by the <u>diaphragm</u>.

3) The <u>lungs</u> are like big pink <u>sponges</u> and are protected by the <u>ribcage</u>. They're surrounded by the <u>pleural membranes</u>.

4) The air that you breathe in goes through the <u>trachea</u>. This splits into two tubes called <u>bronchi</u> (each one is a bronchus), one going to each lung.

5) The bronchi split into progressively smaller tubes called <u>bronchioles</u>.

6) The bronchioles finally end at small bags called <u>alveoli</u> where the gas exchange takes place (see next page).

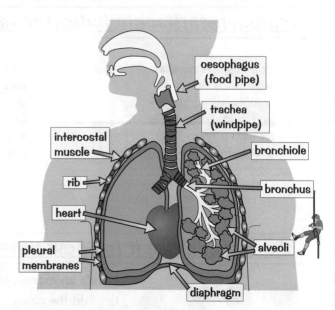

Breathing In...

1) <u>Intercostal muscles</u> and <u>diaphragm contract</u>.

2) Thorax volume <u>increases</u>.

3) This decreases the pressure, drawing air <u>in</u>.

...and Breathing Out

1) <u>Intercostal muscles</u> and <u>diaphragm relax</u>.

2) Thorax volume <u>decreases</u>.

3) Air is forced <u>out</u>.

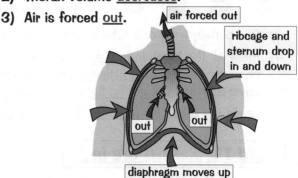

You Can Investigate the Effect of Exercise on Breathing Rate

1) There's a really simple experiment you can do to see what happens to breathing rate when you exercise:

- Firstly, <u>sit still</u> for <u>five minutes</u>. Then, for <u>one minute</u>, count the <u>number of breaths</u> you take.

- Now do <u>four minutes</u> of <u>exercise</u> (running, skipping, Mexican waving...) and as soon as you stop <u>count your breaths</u> for a minute.

- Pester <u>two other people</u> to do the same so you get three sets of results to compare.

2) Your results should show that exercise <u>increases breathing rate</u>. This is because your <u>muscles respire more</u> during exercise. They need to be supplied with <u>more O$_2$</u> and have <u>more CO$_2$</u> removed (see p.28), so your breathing rate increases.

3) During this experiment you need to <u>control all the variables</u> that might affect your results — e.g. you can control the <u>time spent exercising</u> using a stopwatch and the <u>temperature</u> of the room using air conditioning (ooh, fancy) or a thermostat.

Stop huffing and puffing and just learn it...

So when you breathe in, you don't have to suck the air in. You just make the <u>space in your lungs bigger</u> and the <u>air rushes in to fill it</u>. Once you've got this page learned, flip over. And don't forget to breathe...

Gas Exchange — Humans

Gas exchange doesn't only happen in plants — it happens in humans too.
Oxygen goes into your bloodstream and you offload nasty 'orrible carbon dioxide...

Alveoli Carry Out Gas Exchange in the Body

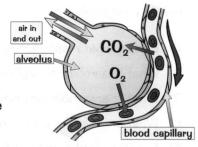

1) The lungs contain millions and millions of little air sacs called alveoli where gas exchange happens.

2) The blood passing next to the alveoli has just returned to the lungs from the rest of the body, so it contains lots of carbon dioxide and very little oxygen. Oxygen diffuses out of the alveolus (high concentration) into the blood (low concentration). Carbon dioxide diffuses out of the blood (high concentration) into the alveolus (low concentration) to be breathed out.

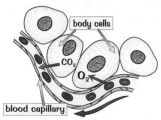

3) When the blood reaches body cells oxygen is released from the red blood cells (where there's a high concentration) and diffuses into the body cells (where the concentration is low).

4) At the same time, carbon dioxide diffuses out of the body cells (where there's a high concentration) into the blood (where there's a low concentration). It's then carried back to the lungs.

Alveoli are Specialised for Gas Exchange

1) The huge number of microscopic alveoli gives the lungs an enormous surface area.

2) There's a moist lining for gases to dissolve in.

3) The alveoli have very thin walls — only one cell thick, so the gas doesn't have far to diffuse.

4) They have a great blood supply to maintain a high concentration gradient.

5) The walls are permeable — so gases can diffuse across easily.

Smoking Tobacco Can Cause Quite a Few Problems

Smoking can severely affect your lungs and circulatory system. Here's how:

1) Smoking damages the walls inside the alveoli, reducing the surface area for gas exchange and leading to diseases like emphysema.

2) The tar in cigarettes damages the cilia (little hairs) in your lungs and trachea. These hairs, along with mucus, catch a load of dust and bacteria before they reach the lungs. The cilia also help to keep the trachea clear by sweeping mucus back towards the mouth. When these cilia are damaged, chest infections are more likely.

3) Tar also irritates the bronchi and bronchioles, encouraging mucus to be produced which can't be cleared very well by damaged cilia — this causes smoker's cough and chronic bronchitis.

4) The carbon monoxide in cigarette smoke reduces the amount of oxygen the blood can carry. To make up for this, heart rate increases — which leads to an increase in blood pressure. High blood pressure damages the artery walls, making the formation of blood clots more likely. This increases the risk of coronary heart disease (e.g. heart attacks).

5) Tobacco smoke also contains carcinogens — chemicals that can lead to cancer.

Alveoli — those guys are bags of fun...

True fact... no really. They're not so fun if they've been damaged by smoking though... it just really gets them down. So the thing to remember is: not smoking leads to happy, contented alveoli. Simple.

Revision Summary for Section 4

Well that's another section you've got through, nice work. Take a deep breath and have a stretch... I bet you thought about what's going on in your lungs then, didn't you? Well whilst you're at it, have a gaze out of the window and have a think about all those plants working their roots off to pump out oxygen... I'll stop there before I get carried away...

1) Explain what respiration is in a sentence.

2) What is aerobic respiration? Give the word and symbol equations for it.

3) What is anaerobic respiration?

4) What are two drawbacks of anaerobic respiration compared to aerobic respiration?

5) Give the word equations for anaerobic respiration in:

   a) animals,

   b) plants.

6) Name an indicator solution that can be used to detect carbon dioxide.

7) Describe an experiment to detect CO_2 production from respiration.

8) Describe an experiment used to monitor the heat produced by respiration.

9) Name the process by which plants exchange gases.

10) Why do plants need to exchange gases with their surroundings?

11) a) At night, there's a lot of O_2 inside the leaf and not a lot of CO_2. True or false?

    b) Explain your answer to part a).

12) Explain how leaves are adapted for efficient gas exchange.

13) What are the little holes on the lower surface of leaves called? Explain their role.

14) Describe an experiment you could use to show the effect of light on gas exchange in leaves. What would you use as a control?

15) Name the key structures of the respiratory system.

16) What happens to the intercostal muscles and diaphragm when you breathe in?

17) What happens to the intercostal muscles and diaphragm when you breathe out?

18) Explain why exercise increases your breathing rate.

19) Describe the gas exchange that happens between the alveoli and the blood.

20) Give four ways that the alveoli's structure is ideal for gas exchange.

21) How does smoking contribute to coronary heart disease?

22) Name two other diseases linked to smoking tobacco.

Functions of the Blood

All <u>multicellular organisms</u> need a <u>transport system</u> (see page 24) and in humans, it's the <u>blood</u>.

Blood has Four Main Components

They are:

PLASMA	PLATELETS	RED BLOOD CELLS	WHITE BLOOD CELLS

Plasma is the Liquid Bit of Blood

It's basically blood minus the blood cells (see below and on the next page). Plasma is a pale yellow liquid which <u>carries just about everything</u> that needs transporting around your body:

1) <u>Red</u> and <u>white blood cells</u> and <u>platelets</u>.
2) <u>Digested food products</u> (like glucose and amino acids) from the gut to all the body cells.
3) <u>Carbon dioxide</u> from the body cells to the lungs.
4) <u>Urea</u> from the liver to the kidneys (where it's removed in the urine, see page 40).
5) <u>Hormones</u>, which act as chemical messengers (see page 46).
6) <u>Heat energy</u>.

Platelets are Small Fragments of Cells that Help Blood Clot

1) When you damage a blood vessel, <u>platelets</u> clump together to 'plug' the damaged area.
2) This is known as <u>blood clotting</u>. Blood clots <u>stop you losing</u> too much <u>blood</u> and prevent <u>microorganisms</u> from entering the wound.
3) In a clot, platelets are held together by a mesh of a protein called <u>fibrin</u> (though this process also needs other proteins called <u>clotting factors</u> to work properly).

Red Blood Cells Have the Job of Carrying Oxygen

They transport <u>oxygen</u> from the <u>lungs</u> to <u>all</u> the cells in the body.
A red blood cell is <u>well adapted</u> to its <u>function</u>:

1) Red blood cells are <u>small</u> and have a <u>biconcave shape</u> (which is a posh way of saying they look a little bit like doughnuts, see diagram below) to give a <u>large surface area</u> for <u>absorbing</u> and <u>releasing oxygen</u>.
2) They contain <u>haemoglobin</u>, which is what gives blood its <u>colour</u> — it contains a lot of <u>iron</u>. In the lungs, haemoglobin <u>reacts with oxygen</u> to become <u>oxyhaemoglobin</u>. In body tissues the reverse reaction happens to <u>release oxygen to the cells</u>.
3) Red blood cells don't have a <u>nucleus</u> — this frees up <u>space</u> for more haemoglobin, so they can carry more oxygen.

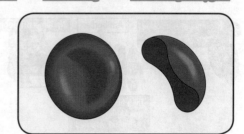

Blood's other function is to let you know you're bleeding...

This book's got more <u>blood and gore</u> than your average horror movie, but I'm afraid you're not allowed to hide <u>behind the sofa</u> — you need to keep your eyes open and your wits about you. By the way, if you're thinking that this book's got less <u>humour</u> than your average comedy, that's because the ~~best~~ rude bits get <u>cut out</u>.

White Blood Cells and Immunity

Your body is constantly fighting off attack from all sorts of nasties — yep, things really are out to get you.

Your Immune System Deals with Pathogens

1) Pathogens are microorganisms that cause disease, e.g. certain types of bacteria and viruses (see p.4).

2) Once pathogens have entered your body they'll reproduce rapidly unless they're destroyed. That's the job of your immune system, and white blood cells are the most important part of it.

3) There are two different types of white blood cell you need to know about: phagocytes and lymphocytes.

Phagocytes Ingest Pathogens

1) Phagocytes detect things that are 'foreign' to the body, e.g. pathogens. They then engulf the pathogens and digest them.

2) Phagocytes are non-specific — they attack anything that's not meant to be there.

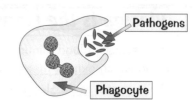

Lymphocytes Produce Antibodies

1) Every pathogen has unique molecules (called antigens) on its surface.

2) When certain white blood cells, called lymphocytes, come across a foreign antigen, they will start to produce proteins called antibodies — these lock on to the invading pathogens and mark them out for destruction by other white blood cells. The antibodies produced are specific to that type of antigen — they won't lock on to any others.

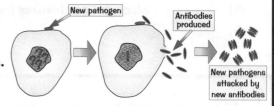

3) Antibodies are then produced rapidly and flow round the body to mark all similar pathogens.

4) Some of these lymphocytes stay around in the blood as memory cells after the original infection has been fought off. They can reproduce very fast if the same antigen enters the body a second time. That's why you're immune to most diseases if you've already had them — the body carries a "memory" of what the antigen was like, and can quickly produce loads of antibodies if you get infected again.

Vaccination — Protects from Future Infections

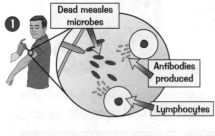

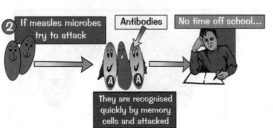

1) When you're infected with a new pathogen it can take your lymphocytes a while to produce the antibodies to deal with it. In that time you can get very ill, or maybe even die.

2) To avoid this you can be vaccinated against some diseases, e.g. polio or measles.

3) Vaccination involves injecting dead or inactive pathogens into the body. These carry antigens, so even though they're harmless they still trigger an immune response — your lymphocytes produce antibodies to attack them.

4) Some of these lymphocytes will remain in the blood as memory cells so if live pathogens of the same type ever appear, the antibodies to kill them will be produced much faster and in greater numbers.

Revision summaries are a lot like vaccinations...

We expose you to some harmless questions (the vaccine) that you learn how to recognise and answer, then when you're confronted with the real exam (the full strength pathogen), you've got the necessary knowledge (memory cells and antibodies) to answer (kill) them. Gosh that was a good analogy — if I may say so myself...

Paper 2

Blood Vessels

Blood needs a good set of 'tubes' to carry it round the body. Here's a page on the different types:

Blood Vessels are Designed for Their Function

There are three different types of blood vessel:

1) ARTERIES — these carry the blood away from the heart.
2) CAPILLARIES — these are involved in the exchange of materials at the tissues.
3) VEINS — these carry the blood to the heart.

Arteries Carry Blood Under Pressure

1) The heart pumps the blood out at high pressure so the artery walls are strong and elastic.

2) The walls are thick compared to the size of the hole down the middle (the "lumen" — silly name). They contain thick layers of muscle to make them strong.

3) The largest artery in the body is the aorta (see next page).

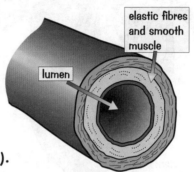

Capillaries are Really Small

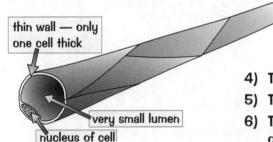

1) Arteries branch into capillaries.

2) Capillaries are really tiny — too small to see.

3) They carry the blood really close to every cell in the body to exchange substances with them.

4) They have permeable walls, so substances can diffuse in and out.

5) They supply food and oxygen, and take away wastes like CO_2.

6) Their walls are usually only one cell thick. This increases the rate of diffusion by decreasing the distance over which it happens.

Veins Take Blood Back to the Heart

1) Capillaries eventually join up to form veins.

2) The blood is at lower pressure in the veins so the walls don't need to be as thick as artery walls.

3) They have a bigger lumen than arteries to help the blood flow despite the lower pressure.

4) They also have valves to help keep the blood flowing in the right direction.

5) The largest vein in the body is the vena cava (see next page).

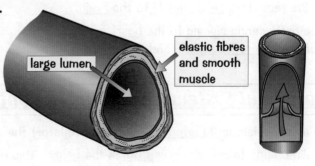

Learn this page — don't struggle in vein...

Here's an interesting fact for you — your body contains about 60 000 miles of blood vessels. That's about six times the distance from London to Sydney in Australia. Of course, capillaries are really tiny, which is how there can be so many miles of them inside you. They can also only be seen under a microscope.

The Heart

Blood doesn't just move around the body <u>on its own</u>, of course. It needs a <u>pump</u>.

Learn **This** Diagram of the Heart **with All Its Labels**

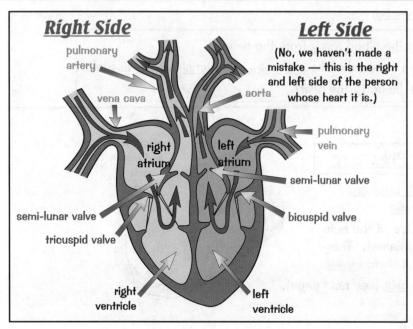

Right Side

pulmonary artery

vena cava

right atrium

semi-lunar valve

tricuspid valve

right ventricle

Left Side

(No, we haven't made a mistake — this is the right and left side of the person whose heart it is.)

aorta

left atrium

pulmonary vein

semi-lunar valve

bicuspid valve

left ventricle

1) The <u>right atrium</u> of the heart receives <u>deoxygenated</u> blood from the <u>body</u> (through the <u>vena cava</u>).
(The plural of atrium is atria.)

2) The deoxygenated blood moves through to the <u>right ventricle</u>, which pumps it to the <u>lungs</u> (via the <u>pulmonary artery</u>).

3) The <u>left atrium</u> receives <u>oxygenated</u> blood from the <u>lungs</u> (through the <u>pulmonary vein</u>).

4) The oxygenated blood then moves through to the <u>left ventricle</u>, which pumps it out round the <u>whole body</u> (via the <u>aorta</u>).

5) The <u>left</u> ventricle has a much <u>thicker wall</u> than the <u>right</u> ventricle.

It needs more <u>muscle</u> because it has to pump blood around the <u>whole body</u>, whereas the right ventricle only has to pump it to the <u>lungs</u>. This also means that the blood in the left ventricle is under <u>higher pressure</u> than the blood in the right ventricle.

6) The <u>valves</u> prevent the <u>backflow</u> of blood.

Exercise **Increases** Heart Rate

1) When you <u>exercise</u>, your muscles need <u>more energy</u>, so you <u>respire more</u>.

2) You need to get <u>more oxygen</u> into the cells and <u>remove</u> more <u>carbon dioxide</u>. For this to happen the blood has to flow faster, so your <u>heart rate increases</u>. Here's how:

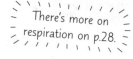
There's more on respiration on p.28.

- Exercise <u>increases</u> the amount of <u>carbon dioxide</u> in the <u>blood</u>.

- High levels of blood CO_2 are detected by <u>receptors</u> in the <u>aorta</u> and <u>carotid artery</u> (an artery in the neck).

- These receptors <u>send signals</u> to the <u>brain</u>.

- The brain sends signals to the <u>heart</u>, causing it to contract <u>more frequently</u> and with <u>more force</u>.

The **Hormonal System** Also Helps to **Control Heart Rate**

1) When an organism is <u>threatened</u> (e.g. by a predator) the <u>adrenal glands</u> release <u>adrenaline</u>.

2) Adrenaline <u>binds</u> to <u>specific receptors</u> in the <u>heart</u>. This causes the cardiac muscle to <u>contract more frequently</u> and with <u>more force</u>, so <u>heart rate increases</u> and the heart <u>pumps more blood</u>.

3) This <u>increases oxygen supply</u> to the <u>tissues</u>, getting the body <u>ready for action</u>.

I ♥ revising...

If you were expecting a <u>smooshy</u>, soppy page about <u>feelings</u> and relationships, I'm sorry to disappoint. You've got to know the <u>inside of your heart</u> like the <u>back of your hand</u>. If you don't bother learning this page, you'll feel pretty <u>silly</u> if you turn over the exam paper and the <u>first question</u> asks you to label a diagram of the heart.

The Circulation System

The circulation system is made up of the heart (see previous page) and the blood vessels. It's responsible for getting the blood to where it needs to be, so that useful substances (e.g. glucose and oxygen) can be delivered and wastes removed. If you didn't have a circulation system, your life would be unimaginably tricky — just like your exam if you don't learn the stuff on this page.

You Need to Know the Structure of the Circulation System

The diagram below shows the human circulation system.
You need to learn the names of all the blood vessels on it for the exam.

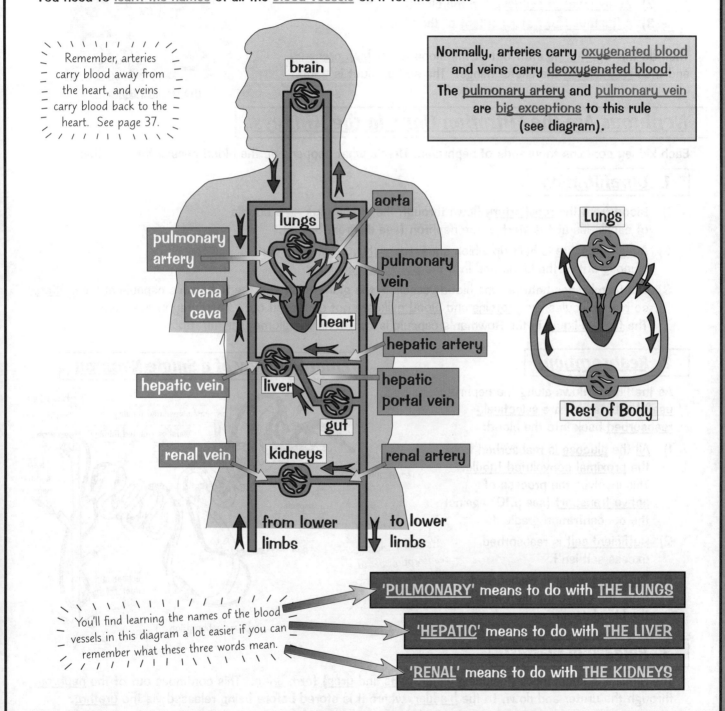

Remember, arteries carry blood away from the heart, and veins carry blood back to the heart. See page 37.

Normally, arteries carry oxygenated blood and veins carry deoxygenated blood.

The pulmonary artery and pulmonary vein are big exceptions to this rule (see diagram).

brain

aorta

lungs

pulmonary artery

pulmonary vein

vena cava

heart

hepatic artery

hepatic vein

liver

hepatic portal vein

gut

renal vein

kidneys

renal artery

from lower limbs

to lower limbs

Lungs

Rest of Body

You'll find learning the names of the blood vessels in this diagram a lot easier if you can remember what these three words mean.

'PULMONARY' means to do with THE LUNGS

'HEPATIC' means to do with THE LIVER

'RENAL' means to do with THE KIDNEYS

The circulation system — named after Sir Q. Lation in 1821...

You need to know the circulation system in a fair bit of detail. You don't need to know all 60 000 miles of it (I'm not even kidding) but you could be asked about how it's laid out and joined up, or the main blood vessels that take blood to and from the heart, the lungs, the liver and the kidneys. As long as you remember that blood in arteries flows away from the heart and blood in veins flows towards it, you're half-way there. Easy peasy.

Excretion — The Kidneys

Excretion (the removal of waste products) is carried out by the skin, the lungs and the kidneys.

The Kidneys are Excretion Organs

The kidneys are part of the urinary system.
They perform three main roles:

1) Removal of urea from the blood. Urea is produced in the liver from excess amino acids.
2) Adjustment of salt levels in the blood.
3) Adjustment of water content of the blood.

They do this by filtering stuff out of the blood under high pressure, and then reabsorbing the useful things. The end product is urine.

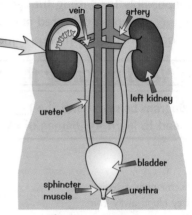

The Urinary System

Nephrons Are the Filtration Units in the Kidneys

Each kidney contains thousands of nephrons. Here's what happens as the blood passes through them:

1. Ultrafiltration:

1) Blood from the renal artery flows through the glomerulus — a bundle of capillaries at the start of the nephron (see diagram below).

2) A high pressure is built up which squeezes water, urea, salts and glucose out of the blood and into the Bowman's capsule.

3) The membranes between the blood vessels in the glomerulus and the Bowman's capsule act like filters, so big molecules like proteins and blood cells are not squeezed out. They stay in the blood. The filtered liquid in the Bowman's capsule is known as the glomerular filtrate.

2. Reabsorption:

As the filtrate flows along the nephron, useful substances are selectively reabsorbed back into the blood:

1) All the glucose is reabsorbed from the proximal convoluted tubule. This involves the process of active transport (see p.10) against the concentration gradient.

2) Sufficient salt is reabsorbed. Excess salt isn't.

3) Sufficient water is reabsorbed from the collecting duct into the bloodstream.

It's called selective reabsorption because only some substances are reabsorbed.

Enlarged View of a Single Nephron

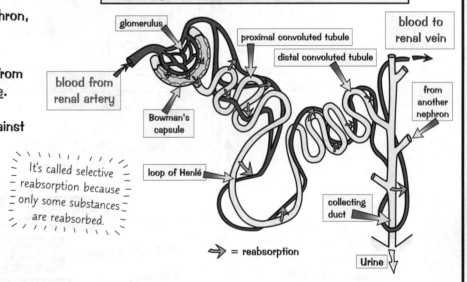

= reabsorption

3. Release of wastes:

The remaining substances (including water, salts and urea) form urine. This continues out of the nephron, through the ureter and down to the bladder, where it is stored before being released via the urethra.

Removal of urea — nothing to do with Vincent van Gogh...

Scientists have made a machine which can do the kidneys' job for us — a kidney dialysis machine. People with kidney failure have to use it for 3-4 hours, 3 times a week. Unfortunately it's not something you can carry around in your back pocket, which makes life difficult for people with kidney failure.

Osmoregulation — The Kidneys

The kidneys are <u>really important</u> organs. Not only do they filter the blood (see previous page), they also play a key role in controlling the amount of water inside your body. Whether you're interested in it or not, I'm afraid <u>you need to know this page</u> for your exam — so <u>pay attention</u>.

The Kidneys *Also Adjust the Body's* Water Content

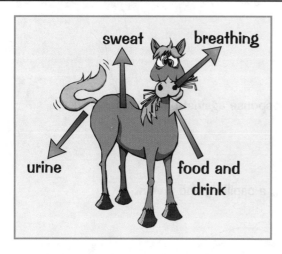

sweat — breathing
urine — food and drink

1) Water is taken into the body as <u>food and drink</u> and is <u>lost</u> from the body in <u>three main ways</u>: sweating, breathing and weeing (see page 47).

2) The body has to <u>constantly balance</u> the water coming <u>in</u> against the water going <u>out</u> — this is <u>osmoregulation</u>.

3) One way that it can do this is by adjusting the amount of water that is <u>excreted by the kidneys</u> in the <u>urine</u>. E.g. If a person is <u>sweating</u> a lot or hasn't <u>drunk</u> enough water, the kidneys can reabsorb more water (see below), so that less is <u>lost in the urine</u> and the water balance is <u>maintained</u>.

ADH *Helps to Control* Water Content

1) The amount of water reabsorbed in the kidney nephrons is <u>controlled</u> by a hormone called <u>anti-diuretic hormone</u> (ADH). ADH makes the nephrons <u>more permeable</u> so more water is <u>reabsorbed</u> back into the blood.

2) The brain <u>monitors the water content of the blood</u> and instructs the <u>pituitary gland</u> to release <u>ADH</u> into the blood according to how much is needed.

3) The whole process of osmoregulation is controlled by a mechanism called <u>negative feedback</u>. This means that if the water content gets <u>too high</u> or <u>too low</u> a mechanism will be triggered that brings it back to <u>normal</u>.

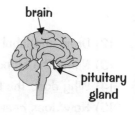

brain

pituitary gland

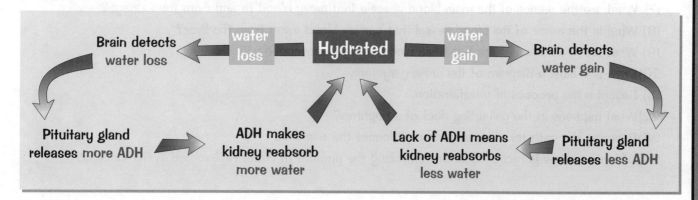

Brain detects water loss ← water loss — Hydrated — water gain → Brain detects water gain

Pituitary gland releases more ADH → ADH makes kidney reabsorb more water — Lack of ADH means kidney reabsorbs less water ← Pituitary gland releases less ADH

Don't try to kid-me that you know it all — learn it properly...

So the kidneys make sure you don't end up like a dry sponge or a massive water balloon — thank goodness. Make sure you remember which way round <u>ADH</u> works. Basically, <u>low</u> blood water content means <u>increased</u> ADH production and <u>more water</u> reabsorbed in the kidneys. <u>High</u> blood water content means <u>decreased</u> ADH production and <u>less water</u> reabsorbed. What could be simpler... erm, actually, let's not get started on that.

Revision Summary for Section 5

It's time to see if any of that went in, or if you were just looking at the pictures and trying to spot the corny jokes. This revision summary should be able to give you an idea of which pages you understand and which ones you're finding a bit trickier. If you get stuck, have another read through the section.

1) What are the four main components of blood?

2) Name six things that blood plasma transports around the body.

3) What are platelets? What role do they play in the body?

4) Explain how red blood cells are adapted to their function.

5) How do phagocytes defend the body from pathogens?

6) How do lymphocytes defend the body from pathogens?

7) Explain the role of memory cells in the immune system's response against pathogens.

8) Explain how vaccination stops you getting infections.

9) Why do arteries need very muscular, elastic walls?

10) Explain how capillaries are adapted to their function.

11)* The diagram below shows cross sections through an artery, a capillary and a vein.
Which one is the vein? How can you tell?

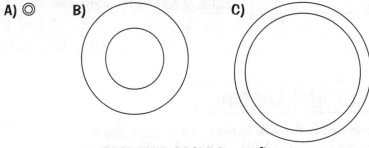

A) ◎   B)   C)

DRAWN TO SCALE (sort of)

12) Draw and label a simple diagram of the heart.

13) Name the blood vessel that joins to the right ventricle of the heart. Where does it take the blood?

14) Why does the left ventricle have a thicker wall than the right ventricle?

15) How does heart rate change during exercise? Why?

16) What hormone causes heart rate to rise?

17) What are the names of the main blood vessels that carry blood to and from the kidneys?

18) What is the name of the blood vessel that carries blood away from the liver?

19) What are the names of the two main blood vessels associated with the lungs?

20) Draw and label a diagram of the urinary system.

21) Describe the process of ultrafiltration.

22) What happens in the collecting duct of a nephron?

23) Describe the path taken by urine once it leaves the nephron.

24) Which hormone is responsible for controlling the amount of water reabsorbed in the kidneys?

* Answers on p. 92

The Nervous System and Responding to Stimuli

Right, it's time to get your brain cells fired up and take a hit of adrenaline — this section's a corker.

Responding to their Environment Helps Organisms Survive

1) Animals increase their chances of survival by responding to changes in their external environment, e.g. by avoiding places that are too hot or too cold.

2) They also respond to changes in their internal environment to make sure that the conditions are always right for their metabolism (all the chemical reactions that go on inside them).

3) Plants also increase their chances of survival by responding to changes in their environment (see page 49).

4) Any change in the internal or external environment is called a STIMULUS.

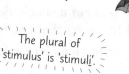

The plural of 'stimulus' is 'stimuli'.

Receptors Detect Stimuli and Effectors Produce a Response

1) RECEPTORS detect stimuli. Receptors in the SENSE ORGANS (the eyes, ears, nose, tongue and skin) are groups of cells that detect external stimuli. E.g. rod and cone cells in the eye detect changes in light (see page 45).

2) EFFECTORS are cells that bring about a response to stimuli. They include muscle cells and cells found in glands, e.g. the pancreas. Effectors respond in different ways — muscle cells contract, whereas glands secrete hormones.

3) Receptors communicate with effectors via the nervous system (see below), the hormonal system (see page 46) or sometimes both.

The Central Nervous System (CNS) Coordinates Information

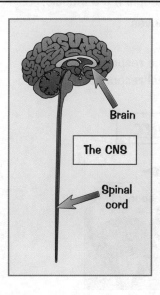

Brain

The CNS

Spinal cord

1) The nervous system is made up of all the neurones (nerve cells) in your body. There are three main types of neurone — sensory neurones, relay neurones and motor neurones.

2) The CENTRAL NERVOUS SYSTEM (CNS) consists of the brain and spinal cord only.

3) When receptors in a sense organ detect a stimulus, they send electrical impulses along sensory neurones to the CNS.

4) The CNS then sends electrical impulses to an effector along a motor neurone. The effector then responds accordingly.

5) The job of the CNS is to COORDINATE the response. Coordinated responses always need a stimulus, a receptor and an effector.

6) Because neurones transmit information using high speed electrical impulses, the nervous system is able to bring about very rapid responses.

If only my broadband was as fast as the CNS...

So without receptors, neurones and effectors you wouldn't be able to respond to your environment. No shivering when you're cold, no pulling your finger back when you prick it and no running away when faced with some revision... don't even think about it — stick around and learn this page. You may as well whilst you're here.

Reflexes

Your brain can <u>decide</u> how to respond to a stimulus <u>pretty quickly</u>. But sometimes waiting for your brain to make a decision is just <u>too slow</u>. That's why you have <u>reflexes</u>.

Reflexes <u>Help</u> Prevent Injury

1) <u>Reflexes</u> are <u>automatic</u> responses to certain stimuli — they can reduce the chances of being injured.

2) For example, if someone shines a <u>bright light</u> in your eyes, your <u>pupils</u> automatically get smaller so that less light gets into the eye — this stops it getting <u>damaged</u> (see next page).

3) Or if you get a shock, your body releases the <u>hormone</u> adrenaline automatically — it doesn't wait for you to <u>decide</u> that you're shocked.

4) The route taken by the information in a reflex (from receptor to effector) is called a <u>reflex arc</u>.

The <u>Reflex</u> Arc <u>Goes</u> <u>Through</u> <u>the</u> <u>Central Nervous System</u>

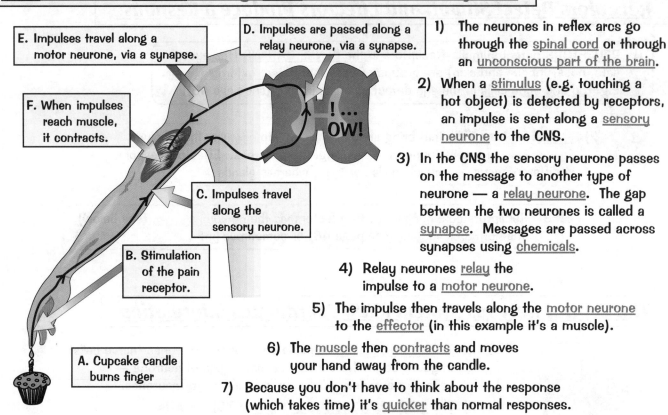

E. Impulses travel along a motor neurone, via a synapse.

D. Impulses are passed along a relay neurone, via a synapse.

F. When impulses reach muscle, it contracts.

C. Impulses travel along the sensory neurone.

B. Stimulation of the pain receptor.

A. Cupcake candle burns finger

! ... OW!

1) The neurones in reflex arcs go through the <u>spinal cord</u> or through an <u>unconscious part of the brain</u>.

2) When a <u>stimulus</u> (e.g. touching a hot object) is detected by receptors, an impulse is sent along a <u>sensory neurone</u> to the CNS.

3) In the CNS the sensory neurone passes on the message to another type of neurone — a <u>relay neurone</u>. The gap between the two neurones is called a <u>synapse</u>. Messages are passed across synapses using <u>chemicals</u>.

4) Relay neurones <u>relay</u> the impulse to a <u>motor neurone</u>.

5) The impulse then travels along the <u>motor neurone</u> to the <u>effector</u> (in this example it's a muscle).

6) The <u>muscle</u> then <u>contracts</u> and moves your hand away from the candle.

7) Because you don't have to think about the response (which takes time) it's <u>quicker</u> than normal responses.

<u>You can Draw a</u> <u>Block Diagram</u> <u>to Represent a</u> <u>Reflex Arc</u>

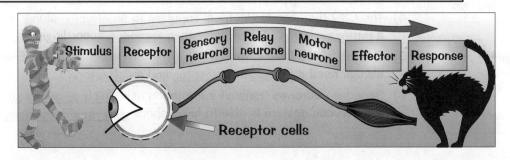

Stimulus | Receptor | Sensory neurone | Relay neurone | Motor neurone | Effector | Response

Receptor cells

<u>Reflex — but only if she hasn't noticed how muscly you are already...</u>

You need to make sure you understand <u>exactly</u> what's going on in a reflex arc. Remember that reflex arcs don't involve the <u>conscious</u> part of the central nervous system — so there's <u>no time wasted</u> while you mess about making a decision. This is what makes them <u>super fast</u> and <u>highly effective</u>.

The Eye

The eye is a good example of a sense organ, and there are several parts you need to learn about.

Learn the Eye with All Its Labels

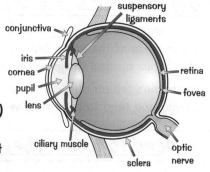

1) The CONJUNCTIVA lubricates and protects the surface of the eye.
2) The CORNEA refracts (bends) light into the eye. The cornea is transparent and has no blood vessels to supply it with oxygen, so oxygen diffuses in from the outer surface.
3) The IRIS controls the diameter of the PUPIL (the hole in the middle) and therefore how much light enters the eye.
4) The LENS focuses the light onto the RETINA (the light-sensitive part — it's covered in light receptors called rods and cones).

   Rods are more sensitive in dim light but can't sense colour. Cones are sensitive to colours but aren't so good in dim light. Cones are found all over the retina, but there are loads of them at the FOVEA.

5) The OPTIC NERVE carries impulses from the receptors to the brain.

The Iris Reflex — Adjusting for Bright Light

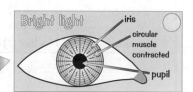

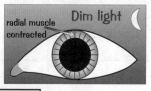

Very bright light can damage the retina — so you have a reflex to protect it.

1) Very bright light triggers a reflex that makes the pupil smaller, allowing less light in. (See the previous page for more about reflexes... but basically, in this case, light receptors detect the bright light and send a message along a sensory neurone to the brain. The message then travels along a relay neurone to a motor neurone, which tells circular muscles in the iris to contract, making the pupil smaller.)

2) The opposite process happens in dim light. This time, the brain tells the radial muscles to contract, which makes the pupil bigger.

Focusing on Near and Distant Objects — Another Reflex

The eye focuses light by changing the shape of the lens — this is known as accommodation.

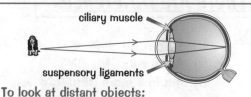

To look at distant objects:
1) The ciliary muscles relax, which allows the suspensory ligaments to pull tight.
2) This makes the lens go thin (less curved).

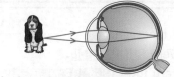

To look at near objects:
1) The ciliary muscles contract, which slackens the suspensory ligaments.
2) The lens becomes fat (more curved).

As you get older, your eye's lens loses flexibility, so it can't easily spring back to a round shape. This means light can't be focused well for near viewing, so older people often have to use reading glasses.

1) Long-sighted people are unable to focus on near objects. This occurs when the cornea or lens doesn't bend the light enough or the eyeball is too short. The images of near objects are brought into focus behind the retina.

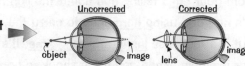

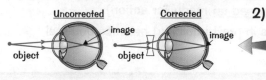

2) Short-sighted people are unable to focus on distant objects. This occurs when the cornea or lens bends the light too much or the eyeball is too long. The images of distant objects are brought into focus in front of the retina.

Eye eye, Captain...

It doesn't matter how good you are at blagging in the exam — you need to learn those diagrams of the eye.

Hormones

The other way to send information around the body (apart from along nerves) is by using hormones.

Hormones Are Chemical Messengers Sent in the Blood

1) Hormones are chemicals released directly into the blood. They're carried in the blood plasma to other parts of the body, but only affect particular cells (called target cells) in particular places. Hormones control things in organs and cells that need constant adjustment.

2) Hormones are produced in various glands. They travel quite slowly and tend to have relatively long-lasting effects.

You Need to Know These Key Hormones and Their Roles in the Body

There are loads of different hormones in the body, each with its own job. The ones in the table below are the really important ones. You need to know where they're made and what they do.

Hormone	Source	Role	Effects
ADH (anti-diuretic hormone)	Pituitary gland (in the brain)	Controls water content.	Increases the permeability of the kidney tubules to water (see p.41).
Adrenaline	Adrenal glands (on top of the kidneys)	Readies the body for a 'fight or flight' response (see below).	Increases heart rate, blood flow to muscles and blood sugar level.
Insulin	Pancreas	Helps control the blood sugar level.	Stimulates the liver to turn glucose into glycogen for storage.
Testosterone	Testes	Main male sex hormone.	Promotes male secondary sexual characteristics, e.g. facial hair (see p.57).
Progesterone	Ovaries	Supports pregnancy.	Maintains the lining of the uterus (see p.58).
Oestrogen	Ovaries	Main female sex hormone.	Controls the menstrual cycle and promotes female secondary sexual characteristics, e.g. widening of the hips (see pages 57 and 58).

Hormones and Nerves Do Similar Jobs, but There Are Differences

NERVES:
1) Very FAST message.
2) Act for a very SHORT TIME.
3) Act on a very PRECISE AREA.

HORMONES:
1) SLOWER message.
2) Act for a LONG TIME.
3) Act in a more GENERAL way.

So if you're not sure whether a response is nervous or hormonal, have a think...

1) If the response is really quick, it's probably nervous.

2) Some information needs to be passed to effectors really quickly (e.g. pain signals, or information from your eyes telling you about the lion heading your way).

3) It's no good using hormones to carry the message — they're too slow.

4) But if a response lasts for a long time, it's probably hormonal.

5) For example, when you get a shock, a hormone called adrenaline is released into the bloodstream (causing the fight-or-flight response, where your body is hyped up ready for action).

6) You can tell it's a hormonal response (even though it kicks in pretty quickly) because you feel a bit wobbly for a while afterwards.

Testes — not quite as bad as examies...

Hormones control various organs and cells in the body, though they tend to control things that aren't immediately life-threatening. For example, they take care of most things to do with sexual development, pregnancy, birth, breast-feeding, blood sugar level, water content... Their effects also tend to be fairly long lasting.

Homeostasis

Homeostasis involves balancing body functions to maintain a "constant internal environment".
Hormones are sometimes (but not always) involved.

Homeostasis — it's all about Balance

Conditions in your body need to be kept steady so that cells can function properly. This involves
balancing inputs (stuff going into your body) with outputs (stuff leaving). For example...

1) Water content — you need to keep a balance between
   the water you gain and the water you lose (see below).

2) Body temperature — you need to get rid of excess body heat
   when you're hot, but retain heat when the environment is cold.

Homeostasis is what keeps these conditions balanced. Don't forget:

Homeostasis is the maintenance of a constant internal environment.

Water Is Lost from the Body in Various Ways

Water is taken into the body as food and drink and is lost from the body in the following ways:

1) through the SKIN as SWEAT...
2) via the LUNGS in BREATH...
3) via the kidneys as URINE.

Some water is also
lost in faeces.

The balance between sweat and urine can depend on what you're doing, or what the weather's like...

- On a HOT DAY, or when you're EXERCISING, you sweat a lot.
- You will produce less urine, but this will be more concentrated (and hence a deeper colour).
- You will also lose more water through your breath when you exercise because you breathe faster.

- On a COLD DAY, or when you're NOT EXERCISING, you don't sweat much.
- You'll produce more urine, which will be pale (since the waste carried in the urine is more diluted).

Body Temperature is Kept at About 37 °C

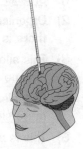

1) All enzymes work best at a certain optimum temperature (see page 5). The enzymes in
   the human body work best at about 37 °C — and so this is the temperature your body
   tries to maintain.

2) A part of the brain acts as your own personal thermostat. It's sensitive to the blood
   temperature in the brain, and it receives messages from temperature receptors in the skin
   that provide information about skin temperature.

3) Based on the signals from these receptors, your central nervous system can activate the
   necessary effectors to make sure your body temperature stays just right.

"I've just had a massive glass of water — I'm going to time homeostasis..."

As you're reading this book, your body is checking the levels of all sorts of variables and tweaking them so that
the conditions are spot on for your body's enzymes to work perfectly. If this wasn't happening, you'd be in real
trouble. It's a delicate balance, but luckily you don't have to concentrate on it — your body does it all for you.

More On Homeostasis

Homeostasis is so important for organisms (and for science students) that I just couldn't resist writing a second page on it for you. If you enjoy reading it half as much as I enjoyed writing it — you're in for a treat.

The Skin Plays an Important Role in Maintaining Body Temperature

To stay at a cosy-but-not-too-warm 37 °C your body has a few tricks up its sleeve:

When You're TOO HOT:

1) Lots of sweat is produced — when it evaporates it transfers heat from you to the environment, cooling you down.
2) Blood vessels close to the surface of the skin widen — this is called vasodilation. It allows more blood to flow near the surface, so it can radiate more heat into the surroundings.
3) Hairs lie flat.

When You're TOO COLD:

1) Very little sweat is produced.
2) Blood vessels near the surface constrict (vasoconstriction) so that less heat can be transferred from the blood to the surroundings.
3) You shiver, and the movement generates heat in the muscles. Exercise does the same.
4) Hairs stand on end to trap an insulating layer of air which helps keep you warm.

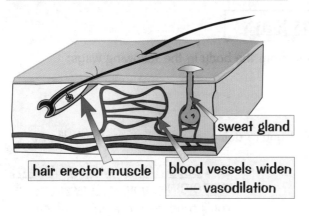

hair erector muscle

sweat gland

blood vessels widen — vasodilation

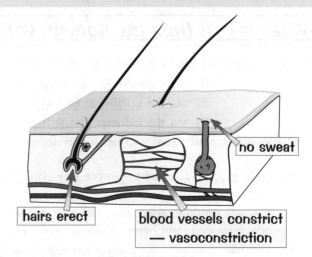

no sweat

hairs erect

blood vessels constrict — vasoconstriction

Smaller Organisms Can Cool Down Quicker

1) Smaller organisms have bigger surface area to volume ratios (see page 10).
2) Organisms with bigger surface area to volume ratios can gain (or lose) heat faster because there is more area for the heat to transfer across.
3) This allows small organisms to lose body heat more easily in hot climates and reduces the chance of them overheating. It also means that they're very vulnerable in cold environments.
4) Organisms with smaller surface area to volume ratios gain (or lose) heat more slowly because there is less area for the heat to transfer across.
5) This is why animals living in cold conditions have a compact (rounded) shape to keep their surface area to a minimum, reducing heat loss.

O homeo(stasis), homeo(stasis)! Wherefore art thou homeo(stasis)?...

So that's why elephants have big ears — to increase their surface area to volume ratios and help them cool down quicker. You learn something new everyday, eh. Which is lucky, what with your exams and everything.

Responses in Plants

You're <u>nearly</u> done for this section. Just this <u>little bit</u> about plants still to go — they're just as important...

Plants **Need to Respond to Stimuli Too**

1) Plants, like animals, <u>increase</u> their chances of <u>survival</u> by responding to changes in their environment, e.g:

- They sense the direction of <u>light</u> and <u>grow</u> towards it to <u>maximise</u> light absorption for <u>photosynthesis</u>.
- They can sense <u>gravity</u>, so their roots and shoots <u>grow</u> in the <u>right direction</u>.
- <u>Climbing</u> plants have a sense of <u>touch</u>, so they can find things to climb and <u>reach</u> the <u>sunlight</u>.

2) Plants are more likely to survive if they respond to the presence of <u>predators</u> to avoid being eaten, e.g.:

<u>White clover</u> is a plant that can produce substances that are <u>toxic</u> to <u>cattle</u>. Cattle start to <u>eat</u> lots of white clover when fields are <u>overgrazed</u> — the white clover <u>responds</u> by <u>producing toxins</u>, to <u>avoid</u> being <u>eaten</u>.

3) Plants are more likely to survive if they respond to abiotic stress — anything harmful that's natural but non-living, like a drought. E.g. some plants respond to extreme cold by producing their own form of antifreeze:

<u>Carrots</u> produce <u>antifreeze proteins</u> at low temperatures — the proteins <u>bind</u> to <u>ice crystals</u> and <u>lower</u> the <u>temperature</u> that water <u>freezes</u> at, <u>stopping</u> more ice crystals from <u>growing</u>.

Auxins **are Plant** Growth Hormones

1) <u>Auxins</u> are <u>plant hormones</u> which control <u>growth</u> at the <u>tips</u> of <u>shoots</u> and <u>roots</u>. They move through the plant in <u>solution</u> (dissolved in water).

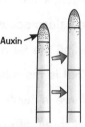

2) Auxin is produced in the <u>tips</u> and <u>diffuses backwards</u> to stimulate the <u>cell elongation process</u> which occurs in the cells <u>just behind</u> the tips.

3) Auxin <u>promotes</u> growth in the <u>shoot</u>, but actually <u>inhibits</u> growth in the <u>root</u>.

4) Auxins are involved in the <u>growth</u> responses of plants to <u>light</u> (phototropism) and <u>gravity</u> (geotropism).

Auxins **Change the** Direction **of Root and Shoot Growth**

SHOOTS ARE POSITIVELY PHOTOTROPIC (grow towards light)

1) When a <u>shoot tip</u> is exposed to <u>light</u>, it accumulates <u>more auxin</u> on the side that's in the <u>shade</u> than the side that's in the <u>light</u>.

2) This makes the cells grow (elongate) <u>faster</u> on the <u>shaded side</u>, so the shoot bends <u>towards</u> the light.

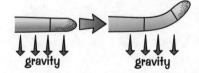

SHOOTS ARE NEGATIVELY GEOTROPIC (grow away from gravity)

1) When a <u>shoot</u> is growing sideways, <u>gravity</u> produces an unequal distribution of auxin in the tip, with <u>more auxin</u> on the <u>lower side</u>.

2) This causes the lower side to grow <u>faster</u>, bending the shoot <u>upwards</u>.

ROOTS ARE POSITIVELY GEOTROPIC (grow towards gravity)

1) A <u>root</u> growing sideways will also have more auxin on its <u>lower side</u>.

2) But in a root the <u>extra</u> auxin <u>inhibits</u> growth. This means the cells on <u>top</u> elongate faster, and the root bends <u>downwards</u>.

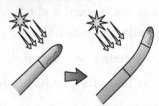

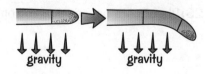

I bet I can guess your response to learning about plants...

Everyone seems to think that plants are <u>boring</u>, but they're actually pretty <u>amazing</u>. They can sense their environment and respond to it accordingly — and they don't even have a nervous system. <u>Unbelievable</u>...

Revision Summary for Section 6

So, you think you're ready to start revising Section 7... Well I've got news for you: The portal behind this page is sealed and (due to some sort of curse involving a very long-winded and unlikely explanation) I have to guard it. If you can answer the following riddles, you may continue on your quest for biological knowledge... (If you can't, have another look at the section and give them another go.) Good luck.

1) Why do organisms respond to changes in their environment?

2) What is a stimulus? How are stimuli detected?

3) Give two types of effector.

4) What does the central nervous system do? What does it consist of?

5) What is the purpose of a reflex action?

6) Describe the pathway of a reflex arc from stimulus to response.

7) Draw a labelled diagram of a human eye.

8) Explain the roles of the following parts of the eye:
    a) cornea
    b) iris
    c) lens

9) Describe the iris reflex. Why is this needed?

10) How does accommodation of the eye work? Is the lens fat or thin to look at distant objects?

11) Define the term 'hormone'.

12) What is the role of the hormone adrenaline? What effects does it have on the body ?

13) Where is insulin made? Describe insulin's role in the body.

14) List three differences between nervous and hormonal responses.

15) Define homeostasis.

16) Write down two conditions that the body needs to keep fairly constant.

17) Give three ways in which water is lost from the body.

18) Describe how the amount and concentration of urine you produce varies depending on how much exercise you do and how hot it is.

19) At what temperature do most of the enzymes in the human body work best?

20) Describe how body temperature is reduced when you're too hot. What happens if you're too cold?

21) Do larger animals tend to have small or large surface area to volume ratios? How does this affect their temperature control?

22) Give two ways in which plants respond to stimuli.

23) What are auxins?

24) What is: a) positive phototropism?   b) positive geotropism?

25) Shoots are negatively geotropic. How are auxins responsible for this?

DNA, Genes and Chromosomes

This page is a little bit tricky, so take your time. It's dead important you get to grips with all this stuff — you're going to need it to understand the rest of the section properly...

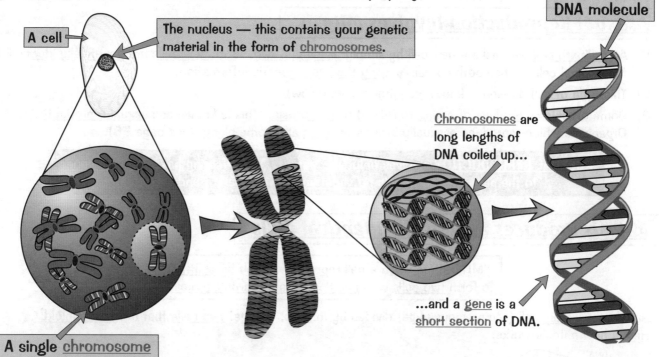

DNA molecule

A cell

The nucleus — this contains your genetic material in the form of chromosomes.

Chromosomes are long lengths of DNA coiled up...

...and a gene is a short section of DNA.

A single chromosome

Human body cells are diploid — this means they have two copies of each chromosome, arranged in pairs. A human cell nucleus contains 46 chromosomes in total — so the diploid number for a human is 46.

Genes are Chemical Instructions

1) DNA is a long list of instructions on how to put an organism together and make it work.

2) Each separate gene in a DNA molecule is a chemical instruction that codes for (says how to make) a particular protein.

3) Proteins are important because they control most processes in the body. They also determine inherited characteristics, e.g. eye colour, blood type.

4) By controlling the production of proteins, genes also control our inherited characteristics.

5) There can be different versions of the same gene, which give different versions of a characteristic — like blue or brown eyes. The different versions of the same gene are called alleles.

DNA is a Double Helix

1) A DNA molecule has two strands coiled together in the shape of a double helix (two spirals).

2) The two strands are held together by chemicals called bases. There are four different bases (shown in the diagram as different colours) — adenine (A), cytosine (C), guanine (G) and thymine (T).

3) The bases are paired, and they always pair up in the same way — it's always A-T and C-G. This is called complementary base-pairing.

4) DNA is a type of nucleic acid.

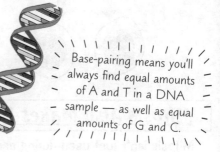

Base-pairing means you'll always find equal amounts of A and T in a DNA sample — as well as equal amounts of G and C.

Genes — they always come in pairs...

Genes are important because they control what characteristics parents pass on to their kids. It's all to do with proteins — genes control the proteins that are made, and proteins control most processes in the body.

Asexual Reproduction and Mitosis

There are two ways an organism can reproduce (asexually and sexually) and two ways a cell can divide (mitosis and meiosis). This page, as you might have guessed, is about asexual reproduction and mitosis.

Asexual Reproduction *Involves Mitosis*

1) An ordinary cell can make a new cell by simply dividing in two. Both new cells are genetically identical to the original cell — they both contain exactly the same genetic information.

2) This type of cell division is known as mitosis (see below).

3) Some organisms produce offspring (children) using mitosis. This is known as asexual reproduction. Organisms which reproduce asexually include bacteria and some plants (see page 56).

> ASEXUAL REPRODUCTION involves only ONE parent. The offspring have identical genes to the parent — so there's no variation between parent and offspring.

Mitosis *Produces Genetically Identical Cells*

> "MITOSIS is when a cell reproduces itself by splitting to form two cells with identical sets of chromosomes."

So when a diploid cell (see previous page) divides by mitosis, you get two cells that are both diploid. Here's how mitosis works:

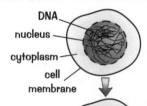

DNA
nucleus
cytoplasm
cell membrane

In a cell that's not dividing, the DNA is all spread out in long strings.

If the cell gets a signal to divide, it needs to duplicate its DNA — so there's one copy for each new cell. The DNA forms X-shaped chromosomes. Each 'arm' of the chromosome is an exact duplicate of the other.

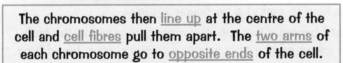

The left arm has the same DNA as the right arm of the chromosome.

The chromosomes then line up at the centre of the cell and cell fibres pull them apart. The two arms of each chromosome go to opposite ends of the cell.

Membranes form around each of the sets of chromosomes. These become the nuclei of the two new cells.

Lastly, the cytoplasm divides.

You now have two new cells containing exactly the same DNA — they're genetically identical.

Mitosis *Also Makes New Cells for Growth and Repair*

Mitosis isn't just used during asexual reproduction — it's how all plants and animals grow and repair damaged tissue. Cloning (see page 81) also involves mitosis.

A cell's favourite computer game — Divide and Conquer...

So, asexual reproduction takes place using mitosis. There's only one parent involved and the offspring are genetically identical to the parent. Lovely. Now for some variation — time for a bit of sexual reproduction...

Sexual Reproduction and Meiosis

Another page, another form of reproduction... Oh, and another type of cell division too. You lucky thing.

Sexual Reproduction Produces Genetically Different Cells

1) Sexual reproduction is where genetic information from two organisms (a father and a mother) is combined to produce offspring which are genetically different to either parent.

2) In sexual reproduction the mother and father produce gametes. Gametes are sperm cells and egg cells.

3) Gametes are haploid — this means they have half the number of chromosomes in a normal cell. In humans, each gamete contains 23 chromosomes — so the haploid number is 23.

4) At fertilisation, a male gamete fuses with a female gamete to form a zygote (fertilised egg). The zygote ends up with the full set of chromosomes.

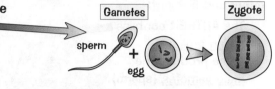

5) The zygote then undergoes cell division (by mitosis — see previous page) and develops into an embryo.

6) The embryo inherits features from both parents — it's received a mixture of chromosomes from its mum and its dad (and it's the chromosomes that decide how you turn out).

7) The fertilisation of gametes is random — this produces genetic variation in the offspring.

> So... SEXUAL REPRODUCTION involves the fusion of male and female gametes.
> Because there are TWO parents, the offspring contain a mixture of their parents' genes.

Gametes are Produced by Meiosis

Meiosis is another type of cell division. It's different to mitosis (on the previous page) because it doesn't produce identical cells. In humans, meiosis only happens in the reproductive organs (ovaries and testes).

> "MEIOSIS produces four haploid cells whose chromosomes are NOT identical."

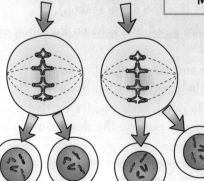

chromosome pair

Meiosis — Division 1

1) Before the cell starts to divide, it duplicates its DNA (so there's enough for each new cell). One arm of each chromosome is an exact copy of the other arm.

2) In the first division in meiosis (there are two divisions) the chromosomes line up in pairs in the centre of the cell.

Step 1 is like the start of mitosis. Step 2 is different though.

3) The pairs are then pulled apart, so each new cell only has one copy of each chromosome. Some of the father's chromosomes (shown in blue) and some of the mother's chromosomes (shown in red) go into each new cell.

4) Each new cell will have a mixture of the mother's and father's chromosomes. Mixing up the genes like this creates variation in the offspring.

Meiosis — Division 2

5) In the second division the chromosomes line up again in the centre of the cell. It's a lot like mitosis. The arms of the chromosomes are pulled apart.

6) You get four haploid gametes — each only has a single set of chromosomes. The gametes are all genetically different.

Sexual Reproduction in Plants

Some types of plants reproduce asexually (see page 52), whilst others reproduce sexually (see below).

The Flower Contains both Male and Female Gametes

Flowering plants have both male and female structures — they're contained in the flower:

The Stamen is the Male Reproductive Part

The stamen consists of the anther and filament:

- The ANTHER contains pollen grains — these produce the male gametes (sperm).
- The FILAMENT is the stalk that supports the anther.

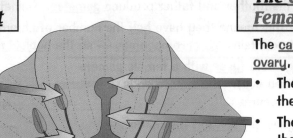

The Carpel is the Female Reproductive Part

The carpel consists of the ovary, style and stigma.

- The STIGMA is the end bit that the pollen grains attach to.
- The STYLE is the rod-like section that supports the stigma.
- The OVARY contains the female gametes (eggs).

1) Pollination is the transfer of pollen from an anther to a stigma, so that the male gametes can fertilise the female gametes (for more on fertilisation in plants, see next page).
2) In sexual reproduction, pollen is transferred from the anther of one plant to the stigma of a different plant. This is known as cross-pollination.
3) Plants that reproduce sexually rely on things like insects or the wind to help them pollinate.

Some Plants are Adapted for Insect Pollination

Here's how plants can be adapted for pollination by insects...

1) They have brightly coloured petals to attract insects.
2) They also have scented flowers and nectaries (glands that secrete nectar) to attract insects.
3) They make big, sticky pollen grains — the grains stick to insects as they go from plant to plant.
4) The stigma is also sticky so that any pollen picked up by insects on other plants will stick to the stigma.

Other Plants are Adapted for Wind Pollination

Features of plants that are adapted for pollination by wind include...

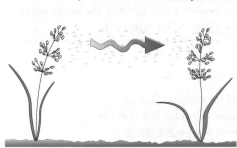

1) Small, dull petals on the flower (they don't need to attract insects).
2) No nectaries or strong scents (for the same reason).
3) A lot of pollen grains — they're small and light so that they can easily be carried by the wind.
4) Long filaments that hang the anthers outside the flower, so that a lot of the pollen gets blown away by the wind.
5) A large and feathery stigma to catch pollen as it's carried past by the wind. The stigma often hangs outside the flower too.

There are no "B"s in wind pollination — bzzzz bzzz bzzzz...

It's a bit weird to think of plants reproducing sexually — it just means that the male gametes (in the pollen) from one plant fertilise the female gametes (in the ovary) of a different plant. Not quite so weird after all.

Fertilisation and Germination in Plants

Once the pollen has found its way to a lovely stigma, it's time for <u>fertilisation</u> to take place...

Fertilisation _is the Fusion of_ Gametes

1) A <u>pollen</u> grain lands on the <u>stigma</u> of a flower, usually with help from insects or the wind (see previous page).

2) A <u>pollen tube</u> grows out of the pollen grain and down through the <u>style</u> to the <u>ovary</u>.

3) A <u>nucleus</u> from the male gamete <u>moves down the tube</u> to join with a female gamete in the <u>ovary</u>. <u>Fertilisation</u> is when the two nuclei <u>fuse</u> together to make a zygote. This divides by mitosis to form an <u>embryo</u>.

4) Each <u>fertilised</u> female gamete forms a <u>seed</u>. The <u>ovary</u> develops into a <u>fruit</u> around the seed.

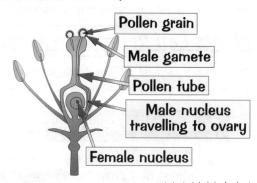

Pollen grain
Male gamete
Pollen tube
Male nucleus travelling to ovary
Female nucleus

Flowering plants can only be fertilised by pollen grains from the same species (or a closely related species).

Germination _is when_ Seeds Start _to_ Grow

A seed will often lie <u>dormant</u> until the <u>conditions</u> around it are right for <u>germination</u>. Seeds need the right <u>conditions</u> to start germinating:

1) <u>Water</u> — to <u>activate</u> the enzymes that <u>break down</u> the <u>food</u> reserves in the seed.

2) <u>Oxygen</u> — for respiration (see page 28), which provides the <u>energy</u> for growth.

3) A suitable <u>temperature</u> — for the enzymes inside the seed to work. This depends on what <u>type</u> of seed it is.

Germination only starts when <u>all</u> these conditions are suitable.

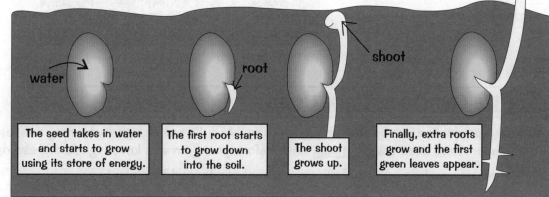

first green leaves

shoot

water

root

The seed takes in water and starts to grow using its store of energy.

The first root starts to grow down into the soil.

The shoot grows up.

Finally, extra roots grow and the first green leaves appear.

Germinating Seeds get Energy _from_ Food Stores

1) A developed seed contains an <u>embryo</u> and a store of <u>food reserves</u>, wrapped in a <u>hard seed coat</u>.

2) When a seed starts to <u>germinate</u>, it gets <u>glucose</u> for respiration from its own <u>food store</u>. This gives it the <u>energy</u> it needs to grow.

3) Once the plant has grown enough to produce <u>green leaves</u> (see above), it can get its own food for energy from <u>photosynthesis</u> (see page 19).

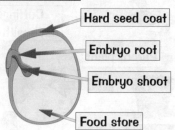

Hard seed coat
Embryo root
Embryo shoot
Food store

Daleks love gardening — ex-germinate, ex-germinate...

Phew, what a palaver. It all starts with <u>flowers</u>, which lead to <u>pollination</u>, then <u>fertilisation</u> and onto <u>seed development</u>. Finally they <u>germinate</u> and blossom into fully-fledged plants surviving on their own far away from their parents. Thank goodness we humans don't make such a <u>song and dance</u> over the same process.

Paper 2

Paper 2

Asexual Reproduction in Plants

Some plants reproduce <u>asexually</u>. They do this in the wild (<u>naturally</u>) and when we force them to (<u>artificially</u>). Artificial asexual reproduction is also called <u>cloning</u>.

Plants Can Reproduce Asexually Using Natural Methods...

Plants have several different ways of reproducing asexually.
Some plants do so by growing <u>new plants</u> from their stems...

> Example: Strawberry Plants
>
> 1) The parent strawberry plant sends out <u>runners</u> — <u>fast-growing</u> <u>stems</u> that grow out <u>sideways</u>, just above the ground.
> 2) The runners <u>take root</u> at various points (a short distance away) and <u>new plants</u> start to grow.
> 3) The new plants are <u>clones</u> of the <u>parent</u> strawberry plant, so there's <u>no</u> genetic variation between them.

Some plants reproduce asexually and sexually, e.g. strawberry plants send out runners and produce fruit (seeds).

runner

new plant

parent plant

Scientifica/Visuals Unlimited, Inc./Getty Images

...or We Can Clone Them Using Artificial Methods

Asexual reproduction can be used to <u>clone plants</u>. And it's not all high-tech crazy science stuff either — gardeners have been using <u>cuttings</u> since before your gran was knee-high to a grasshopper.

1) Gardeners can take <u>cuttings</u> from good parent plants, and then plant them to produce <u>genetically identical copies</u> (clones) of the parent plant.

2) These plants can be produced <u>quickly and cheaply</u>.

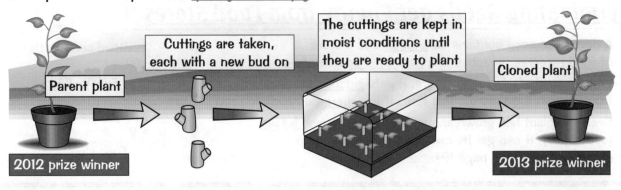

Parent plant

2012 prize winner

Cuttings are taken, each with a new bud on

The cuttings are kept in moist conditions until they are ready to plant

Cloned plant

2013 prize winner

Reproduction doesn't have to involve sex — ask any spider plant...

Other plants can reproduce asexually too, e.g. <u>potatoes</u>, <u>daffodils</u> and <u>spider plants</u>. Spider plants grow tufty bits at the end of their shoots called <u>plantlets</u> — each plantlet is a <u>clone</u> of the original plant. The clone grows roots and becomes a <u>new plant</u>. Plantlets

Human Reproductive Systems

If you skipped to this page in the book first, shame on you... But now you're here, it's time to learn all about the <u>male</u> and <u>female reproductive systems</u> — with a little bit on <u>sex hormones</u> thrown in for good measure.

The Male Reproductive System Makes Sperm

1) Sperm are <u>male gametes</u>. They're made in the <u>testes</u>, <u>all the time</u> after puberty.

2) Sperm mix with a <u>liquid</u> to make <u>semen</u>, which is <u>ejaculated</u> from the penis into the <u>vagina</u> of the female during <u>sexual intercourse</u>.

See page 53 for more on gametes.

<u>Urethra</u> — a tube which carries sperm through the penis during ejaculation. Urine also passes through the urethra to exit the body.

<u>Glands</u> — produce the liquid that's added to sperm to make semen.

<u>Vas deferens</u> (sperm duct) — muscular tube that carries sperm from testis towards the urethra.

<u>Erectile tissue</u> — swells when filled with blood, to make the penis erect.

<u>Head of penis</u>

<u>Foreskin</u> (may be removed)

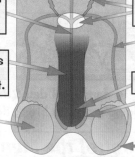

The plural is 'testes'.

<u>Testis</u> — where sperm are made.

<u>Scrotal sac</u> (scrotum) — hangs behind the penis and contains the testes.

The Female Reproductive System Makes Ova (Eggs)

1) Ova are <u>female gametes</u>. An <u>ovum</u> (egg) is produced <u>every 28 days</u> from one of the two <u>ovaries</u>.

2) It then passes into the <u>Fallopian tube</u> — this is where it might <u>meet sperm</u> that have entered the vagina during <u>sexual intercourse</u>.

3) If it <u>isn't fertilised</u> by sperm, the ovum will <u>break up</u> and pass out of the <u>vagina</u>.

4) If it <u>is fertilised</u>, the ovum starts to divide. The new cells will travel down the Fallopian tube to the <u>uterus</u> (womb) and attach to the <u>endometrium</u> (uterus lining). A fertilised ovum develops into an <u>embryo</u>.

<u>Fallopian tube</u> (oviduct) — a muscular tube that carries the ovum from the ovary to the uterus.

Muscular uterus wall

<u>Ovary</u> — the organ that produces ova and sex hormones.

<u>Endometrium</u> (lining of uterus) — has a good blood supply for implantation of an embryo.

<u>Uterus</u> (womb) — the organ where an embryo grows.

<u>Cervix</u> — the neck of the uterus.

<u>Vulva</u>

<u>Vagina</u> — where the sperm are deposited.

Hormones Promote Sexual Characteristics at Puberty

At puberty, your body starts releasing <u>sex hormones</u> — <u>testosterone</u> in men and <u>oestrogen</u> in women. These trigger off the <u>secondary sexual characteristics</u>:

Oestrogen in women causes...

1) <u>Extra hair</u> on underarms and pubic area.
2) <u>Hips</u> to <u>widen</u>.
3) Development of <u>breasts</u>.
4) <u>Ovum</u> release and <u>start of periods</u>.

Testosterone in men causes...

1) <u>Extra hair</u> on face and body.
2) <u>Muscles</u> to <u>develop</u>.
3) <u>Penis and testicles</u> to enlarge.
4) <u>Sperm</u> production.
5) <u>Deepening</u> of <u>voice</u>.

See page 46 for more on hormones.

Phew — who'd be a teenager...

I have my suspicions that you won't have too much difficulty <u>remembering</u> most of this stuff.
Nevertheless, make sure you <u>learn</u> everything on this page, so you don't throw away <u>easy marks</u> in the exam.
Sadly, I don't think you'll get any credit for making it up, even if it is pretty funny.

The Menstrual Cycle and Pregnancy

Starting in <u>puberty</u>, females undergo a monthly sequence of events — the <u>menstrual cycle</u>.
This involves the body <u>preparing</u> the <u>uterus</u> (womb) in case it receives a <u>fertilised ovum</u> (egg).

The Menstrual Cycle has Four Stages

<u>Stage 1</u> <u>Day 1 is when bleeding starts</u>.
The uterus lining breaks down for about
four days.

<u>Stage 2</u> <u>The uterus lining builds up again</u>,
from day 4 to day 14, into a thick spongy
layer full of blood vessels, ready to receive
a fertilised ovum (egg).

<u>Stage 3</u> <u>An ovum develops and is released</u>
from the ovary at day 14.

<u>Stage 4</u> <u>The wall is then maintained</u> for about 14 days until day 28. If no fertilised ovum has landed on the
uterus wall by day 28, the spongy lining starts to break down and the whole cycle starts again.

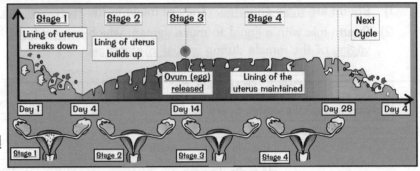

Oestrogen and Progesterone Control the Menstrual Cycle

These two hormones are produced in the <u>ovaries</u>, and they control the main events of the cycle:

1) OESTROGEN:
- Causes the lining of the uterus to <u>thicken</u> and <u>grow</u>.
- Stimulates the <u>release of an ovum</u> at day 14.

It's actually a hormone called
LH which stimulates ovum
release. But oestrogen stimulates
production of LH in the first
place, so this is more or less true.

2) PROGESTERONE: <u>Maintains</u> the lining of the uterus. When the level
of progesterone <u>falls</u>, the lining <u>breaks down</u>.

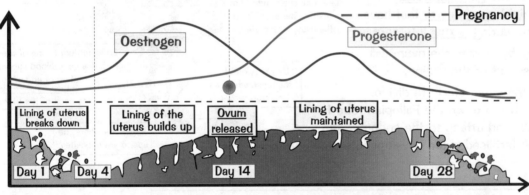

If a fertilised ovum
implants in the uterus
(i.e. the woman
becomes <u>pregnant</u>)
then the level of
<u>progesterone</u> will <u>stay
high</u> to maintain the
lining of the uterus
during pregnancy.

The Embryo Develops During Pregnancy

Once an ovum has been fertilised, it develops into an <u>embryo</u> and implants in the uterus.
In <u>later stages</u> of pregnancy (when it starts to look human) the embryo is called a <u>fetus</u>.

Placenta

Once the embryo has implanted,
the <u>placenta</u> develops — this lets
the blood of the embryo and mother
get very close to allow the exchange
of <u>food</u>, <u>oxygen</u> and <u>waste</u>.

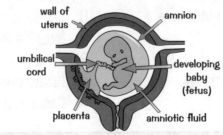

Amniotic Fluid

The <u>amnion membrane forms</u> —
this surrounds the embryo and is
full of <u>amniotic fluid</u>. Amniotic
fluid <u>protects</u> the embryo against
knocks and bumps.

Female or not — you've still got to know all this...
In the exam, you might get graphs like the ones above and be asked to explain <u>which hormone</u> causes <u>what</u>.

Genetic Diagrams

This page is all about how <u>characteristics</u> (like eye colour) are <u>inherited</u>. Before you start, you might want to refresh your memory of <u>genes</u>, <u>chromosomes</u> and <u>DNA</u> on page 51. It'll make life a lot easier, trust me.

Alleles <u>are Different Versions</u> of the Same Gene

1) Most of the time you have <u>two copies</u> of each gene (i.e. <u>two alleles</u>, see p.51) — one from each parent.

2) If the alleles are different, you have <u>instructions</u> for <u>two different versions</u> of a characteristic (e.g. blue eyes or brown eyes) but you only <u>show one version</u> of the two (e.g. brown eyes). The version of the characteristic that appears is caused by the <u>dominant allele</u>. The other allele is said to be <u>recessive</u>. The characteristic caused by the recessive allele only appears if <u>both alleles</u> are recessive.

3) In genetic diagrams, <u>letters</u> are used to represent <u>genes</u>. Dominant alleles are always shown with a <u>capital letter</u> (e.g. 'C') and <u>recessive alleles</u> with a <u>small letter</u> (e.g. 'c').

4) If you're <u>homozygous</u> for a trait you have <u>two alleles the same</u> for that particular gene, e.g. CC or cc. If you're <u>heterozygous</u> for a trait you have <u>two different alleles</u> for that particular gene, e.g. Cc.

> Paper 2 Some characteristics are caused by <u>codominant alleles</u>. Neither allele is recessive, so you <u>show characteristics</u> from <u>both alleles</u> (e.g. not blood group A or B, but blood group <u>AB</u>). Paper 2

5) Your <u>genotype</u> is the <u>alleles</u> that you have. Your <u>phenotype</u> is the <u>characteristics</u> the alleles produce.

Genetic Diagrams <u>show the</u> Possible Alleles <u>in the</u> Offspring

Imagine you're cross-breeding <u>hamsters</u>, and that some have a normal, boring disposition while others have a leaning towards crazy acrobatics. And suppose you know that the behaviour is due to <u>one gene</u>...

Let's say that the allele which causes the crazy nature is <u>recessive</u> — so use a '<u>b</u>'. And normal (boring) behaviour is due to a <u>dominant allele</u> — call it '<u>B</u>'.

1) A <u>crazy</u> hamster <u>must</u> have the <u>genotype bb</u> (i.e. it must be homozygous for this trait).

2) However, a <u>normal hamster</u> could have <u>two</u> possible genotypes — BB (homozygous) or Bb (heterozygous), because the dominant allele (B) <u>overrules</u> the recessive one (b).

3) Here's what happens if you breed from two <u>heterozygous</u> hamsters:

Parents' <u>phenotypes</u>:	normal and boring normal and boring
Parents' <u>genotypes</u>:	Bb Bb
Gametes' <u>genotypes</u>:	B b B b
Offsprings' <u>genotypes</u>:	BB Bb Bb bb
Offsprings' <u>phenotypes</u>:	normal normal normal crazy!

The lines show <u>all</u> the <u>possible</u> ways the parents' alleles <u>could</u> combine. Remember, only <u>one</u> of these possibilities would <u>actually happen</u> for any one offspring.

When you breed two organisms together to look at one characteristic it's called a <u>MONOHYBRID CROSS</u>.

There's a <u>75% chance</u> of having a normal, boring hamster, and a <u>25% chance</u> of a crazy one. To put that another way... you'd expect a <u>3 : 1 ratio</u> of normal : crazy hamsters. This ratio is called a <u>phenotypic ratio</u> (because it's a ratio of different phenotypes).

4) If you breed <u>two homozygous</u> hamsters there's only <u>one possible offspring</u> you can end up with. For example, breeding BB and bb hamsters can only give offspring with a Bb genotype — and they'd all have a normal phenotype.

What do you get if you cross a kangaroo and a sheep...

...a ratio of 1 : 1 kangsheep to sheeparoos... bet you thought I was going to say a woolly jumper. At first glance this stuff can look <u>quite confusing</u>, but the more you <u>go over it</u>, the more it <u>makes sense</u>. Make sure you can predict the <u>outcome</u> of monohybrid crosses, but don't forget that they're only <u>probabilities</u>.

More Genetic Diagrams

Just when you thought it was safe to turn over... Mostly genetic diagrams. Mwa ha haaa. Ahem.
Actually they're really not that bad. And I've given you lots of lovely examples to help you out.

There's Another Way to Draw Genetic Diagrams

You can also draw a type of genetic diagram called a Punnett square.
They're dead easy to do. You start by drawing a grid like this.

Then you fill it in like this:

1) Put the possible gametes from one parent down the side,
and those from the other parent along the top.

2) In each middle square, fill in the letters from the top and side that line up with that square.
The pairs of letters in the middle show the possible combinations of the gametes.

Example:

1) Huntington's is a genetic disorder of the nervous system.
2) The disorder is caused by a dominant allele, 'N', and so can
be inherited if just one parent carries the defective gene.
3) The parent who carries the gene will be a sufferer too since
the allele is dominant, but the symptoms don't start to
appear until after the person is about 40.
4) As the Punnett square shows, a person carrying the N allele
has a 50% chance of passing it on to each of their children.
5) There's also a 1 : 1 phenotypic ratio in the children of
carrier : unaffected child.

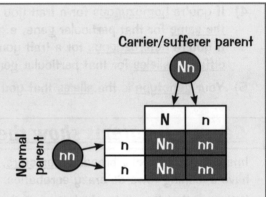

Carrier/sufferer parent

You Can Draw Genetic Diagrams for Codominant Inheritance too

For the Paper 2 exam, you might need to work out the outcome of a
monohybrid cross involving codominant alleles (see previous page).

Don't worry, it's pretty straightforward — you can use a genetic diagram like the ones above to help you.

Here's an example:

Codominant Inheritance of Blood Groups

1) Your blood type is determined by two codominant alleles
(A and B) and one recessive one (O).

2) Blood can be type A (AA or AO genotype), type B (BB or BO
genotype), type AB (AB genotype) or type O (OO genotype).

3) As the Punnett square shows, for two people with type AB blood
there's a 50% chance their children will be type AB, a 25%
chance they'll be type A and a 25% chance they'll be type B.

'O' is a recessive allele,
but it's usually written as
a capital letter. There's an
exception to every rule...

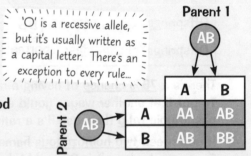

Personally, I prefer strawberries in my Punnett squares...

They might ask you to draw a genetic diagram in the exam. It's nothing to panic about though — they all work
the same way. So go over all the examples on this page (and the previous one) until you're happy with them.

Family Pedigrees and Sex Determination

Bit of a <u>mixed bag</u> this page — still, it makes life just a tad more <u>exciting</u>...

You Need to Understand Family Pedigrees

Knowing how inheritance works helps you to interpret a <u>family pedigree</u> (a family tree of genetic disorders). Here's a worked example using <u>cystic fibrosis</u> — a genetic disorder of the cell membranes.

1) The allele which causes cystic fibrosis is a <u>recessive allele</u>, 'f', carried by about <u>1 person in 30</u>.

2) Because it's recessive, people with only <u>one copy</u> of the allele <u>won't</u> have the disorder — they're known as <u>carriers</u>.

3) For a child to have a chance of inheriting the disorder, <u>both parents</u> must be either <u>carriers</u> or <u>sufferers</u>.

4) As the diagram shows, there's a <u>1 in 4 chance</u> of a child having the disorder if <u>both</u> parents are <u>carriers</u>.

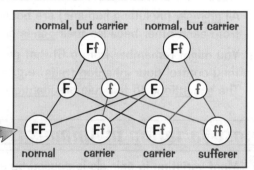

On the right is a <u>family pedigree</u> for a family that includes cystic fibrosis sufferers.

1) The allele for cystic fibrosis <u>isn't</u> dominant because plenty of the family <u>carry</u> the allele but <u>aren't sufferers</u>.

2) There is a <u>25%</u> chance that the new baby will be a sufferer and a <u>50%</u> chance that it will be a carrier because both of its parents are carriers but not sufferers. The case of the new baby is just the same as in the genetic diagram in the box above — so the baby could be <u>normal</u> (FF), a <u>carrier</u> (Ff) or a <u>sufferer</u> (ff).

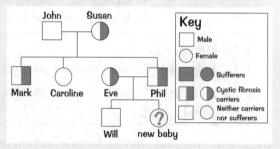

Now for a couple of <u>very important</u> little chromosomes...

Your Chromosomes Control Whether You're Male or Female

There are <u>23 matched pairs</u> of <u>chromosomes</u> in every human body cell. The <u>23rd pair</u> is labelled <u>XX</u> or <u>XY</u>. They're the two chromosomes that decide whether you turn out <u>male</u> or <u>female</u>.

<u>All men</u> have an <u>X</u> and a <u>Y</u> chromosome: **XY** The <u>Y chromosome</u> causes <u>male characteristics</u>.	<u>All women</u> have <u>two X chromosomes</u>: **XX** The <u>XX combination</u> causes <u>female characteristics</u>.

This is true for <u>all mammals</u>, but not for some other organisms, e.g. plants.

There's an Equal Chance of Having a Boy or a Girl...

...and there's a genetic diagram to prove it.

Even though we're talking about inheriting <u>chromosomes</u> here and not single genes, the genetic diagram still works the same way.

When you plug all the letters into the diagram, it shows that there are <u>two XX results</u> and <u>two XY results</u>, so there's the same probability of getting a boy or a girl.

Don't forget that this <u>50 : 50 ratio</u> is only a <u>probability</u>. If you had four kids they <u>could</u> all be <u>boys</u>.

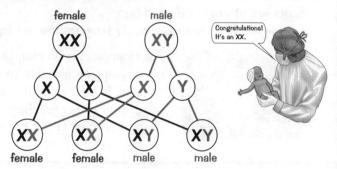

Have you got the Y-factor...

I bet you're sick of genetic diagrams by now. Still, that <u>family pedigree</u> makes a nice change. Umm... sort of.

Variation

The word 'variation' sounds far too fancy for its own good. All it means is how animals or plants of the same species look or behave slightly differently from each other. You know, a bit taller or a bit fatter or a bit more scary-to-look-at etc. There are two kinds of variation — genetic and environmental.

Genetic Variation is Caused by... Genes (Surprise)

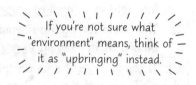
Sexual reproduction produces genetic variation in other species too, e.g. plants.

1) All animals (including humans) are bound to be slightly different from each other because their genes are slightly different.

2) You might remember from p.51 that genes determine how your body turns out — they control your inherited traits, e.g. eye colour. We all end up with a slightly different set of genes. The exceptions to this rule are identical twins, because their genes are exactly the same.

Most Variation in Animals is Due to Genes AND Environment

1) Most variation in animals is caused by a mixture of genetic and environmental factors.

2) Almost every single aspect of a human (or other animal) is affected by our environment in some way, however small. In fact it's a lot easier to list the factors which aren't affected in any way by environment:

- Eye colour,
- Hair colour in most animals (in humans, vanity plays a big part),
- Inherited disorders like haemophilia, cystic fibrosis, etc.,
- Blood group.

If you're not sure what "environment" means, think of it as "upbringing" instead.

3) Environment can have a large effect on human growth even before someone's born. For example, a baby's weight at birth can be affected by the mother's diet.

4) And having a poor diet whilst you're growing up can stunt your growth — another environmental variation.

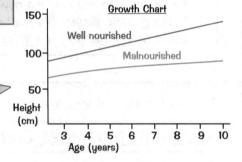

Growth Chart

Well nourished

Malnourished

Height (cm)

150

100

50

Age (years) 3 4 5 6 7 8 9 10

5) For some characteristics, it's hard to say which factor is more important — genes or environment...

- Health — Some people are more likely to get certain diseases (e.g. cancer and heart disease) because of their genes. But lifestyle also affects the risk, e.g. if you smoke or only eat junk food.
- Intelligence — One theory is that although your maximum possible IQ might be determined by your genes, whether you get to it depends on your environment, e.g. your upbringing and school life.
- Sporting ability — Again, genes probably determine your potential, but training is important too.

Environmental Variation in Plants is Much Greater

Plants are strongly affected by:
1) sunlight, 2) moisture level, 3) temperature, 4) the mineral content of the soil.

For example, plants may grow twice as big or twice as fast due to fairly modest changes in environment such as the amount of sunlight or rainfall they're getting, or how warm it is or what the soil is like.

Think about it — if you give your pot plant some plant food (full of lovely minerals), then your plant grows loads faster. Farmers and gardeners use mineral fertilisers to improve crop yields.

Environmental variation — like sun and scattered showers...

So there you go... the "nature versus nurture" debate (the "Are you like you are because of the genes you're born with, or because of the way you're brought up?" debate) summarised in one page. And the winner is... well, both of them really. Your genes are pretty vital, but then so is your environment. What an anticlimax.

Evolution and Natural Selection

The <u>theory of evolution</u> states that one of your (probably very distant) ancestors was a <u>blob</u> in a swamp somewhere. Something like that, anyway. It's probably best to read on for more details...

Make Sure You Know the Theory of Evolution

THEORY OF EVOLUTION: Life began as simple organisms from which more complex organisms evolved (rather than just popping into existence).

The whole <u>process</u> of evolution usually takes place gradually over <u>millions of years</u>. It's still going on today, e.g. some <u>bacteria</u> are evolving to become <u>resistant to antibiotics</u> (see the next page).

Natural Selection Means the "Survival of the Fittest"

<u>Natural selection</u> is one of the key <u>processes</u> that causes <u>evolution</u>. It works like this:

1) Living things show <u>variation</u> — they're <u>not</u> all the same. OK, it's fairly simple so far.

2) The <u>resources</u> living things need to survive are <u>limited</u>. Individuals must <u>compete</u> for these resources to <u>survive</u> — only some of the individuals will survive.

3) Some of the <u>varieties</u> of a particular species will have a <u>better chance</u> of survival. Those varieties will then have an increased chance of <u>breeding</u> and passing on their <u>genes</u>.

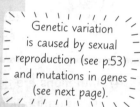

Genetic variation is caused by sexual reproduction (see p.53) and mutations in genes (see next page).

4) This means that a <u>greater</u> proportion of individuals in the next generation will have the better <u>alleles</u>, and so the <u>characteristics</u>, that help <u>survival</u>.

5) Over many generations, the species becomes better and better able to <u>survive</u>. The 'best' features are <u>naturally selected</u> and the species becomes more and more <u>adapted</u> to its environment.

HERE'S AN EXAMPLE

Once upon a time maybe all rabbits had <u>short ears</u> and managed OK. Then one day out popped a rabbit with <u>big ears</u> who could hear better and was always the first to dive for cover at the sound of a predator. Pretty soon he's fathered a whole family of rabbits with <u>big ears</u>, all diving for cover before the other rabbits, and before you know it there are only <u>big-eared</u> rabbits left — because the rest just didn't hear trouble coming quick enough.

This is how populations <u>adapt</u> to survive better in their environment (an organism doesn't actually change when it's alive — changes only occur from generation to generation).

FOX!

Over many generations the <u>characteristic</u> that <u>increases survival</u> becomes <u>more common</u> in the population. If members of a species are separated somehow, and evolve in different ways to adapt to different conditions, then over time you can end up with two totally <u>different species</u>.

The Best Genes for a Particular Environment Tend to Survive

1) The individuals who are <u>less suited</u> to an environment are <u>less likely</u> to survive than those that are better suited, and so have <u>less chance</u> to pass their <u>alleles</u> on. Gradually, over time, this results in a population which is extremely <u>well suited</u> to the environment in which it lives.

2) Remember — <u>variations</u> that are caused by the <u>environment</u> itself (e.g. accidentally losing a finger) <u>aren't</u> involved in natural selection. Variations in a species can have either <u>environmental</u> or <u>genetic causes</u>, but only the <u>genetic</u> ones are passed on to the next generation and influence the <u>evolution</u> of the species.

"Natural Selection" — sounds like vegan chocolates...

It's no good being really great at surviving if for some reason you don't breed and <u>pass on your genes</u>. Also remember that it's only <u>genetic traits</u> that get passed on. So if you have funny ears, but have plastic surgery to make them nicer, your kids can still inherit your old ears, not your new prettier ones.

Mutations and Antibiotic Resistance

You saw on page 62 that everyone is <u>slightly different</u>, partly because of their different <u>environments</u> but also partly because everyone has different <u>genes</u> (apart from identical twins). So, how come we all have different genes? Well, it's partly because of how <u>sexual reproduction</u> works (see page 53) and partly due to <u>mutation</u>.

Mutations are Changes to the Genetic Code

1) <u>Occasionally</u> a gene may <u>mutate</u>. A mutation is a <u>rare</u>, <u>random change</u> in an organism's <u>DNA</u> that can be <u>inherited</u>.

2) Mutations <u>change the sequence</u> of the <u>DNA bases</u> (see page 51). This could <u>stop the production</u> of a <u>protein</u>, or it might mean a <u>different</u> protein is produced instead. This can lead to <u>new characteristics</u>, <u>increasing variation</u>.

3) Mutations can happen <u>spontaneously</u> — when a chromosome doesn't quite copy itself properly. However, the chance of mutation is <u>increased</u> by exposing yourself to:

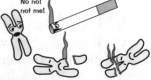

- <u>ionising radiation</u>, e.g. X-rays, gamma rays or ultraviolet light,
- <u>chemicals</u> called <u>mutagens</u>, e.g. chemicals in tobacco.

If the mutations can lead to cancer then the chemicals are called <u>carcinogens</u>.

4) Mutations are <u>usually harmful</u>.
- If a mutation occurs in <u>reproductive cells</u>, the offspring might develop <u>abnormally</u> or <u>die</u>.
- If a mutation occurs in body cells, the mutant cells may start to <u>multiply</u> in an <u>uncontrolled</u> way and <u>invade</u> other parts of the body (which is <u>cancer</u>).

5) <u>Some</u> mutations have <u>no effect</u> at all, for example, if they occur in an <u>unimportant</u> part of the DNA — these mutations are said to be <u>neutral</u>.

6) <u>Very occasionally</u>, mutations are <u>beneficial</u> and give an organism a <u>survival advantage</u>, so it can live on in conditions where the others die. This is <u>natural selection</u> at work (see previous page). For example, a mutation in a bacterium might make it <u>resistant to antibiotics</u>. If this mutant gene is passed on, you might get a <u>resistant</u> "<u>strain</u>" of bacteria, which antibiotics can't kill — see below....

Bacteria can Evolve and Become Antibiotic-Resistant

1) Like all organisms, bacteria sometimes develop <u>random mutations</u> in their DNA. These can lead to <u>changes</u> in the bacteria's characteristics. Sometimes, they mean that a bacterium is <u>less affected</u> by a particular <u>antibiotic</u>.

2) For the bacterium, this ability to resist antibiotics is a big <u>advantage</u>. It's better able to survive, even in a host who's being treated to get rid of the infection, and so it lives for longer and <u>reproduces</u> many more times.

3) This leads to the <u>gene</u> for resistance being <u>passed on</u> to lots of offspring — it's just <u>natural selection</u>. This is how it spreads and becomes <u>more common</u> in a population of bacteria over time.

4) This is a problem for people who become <u>infected</u> with these bacteria, because you <u>can't</u> easily get rid of them with antibiotics. Sometimes drug companies can come up with a <u>new</u> antibiotic that's effective, but '<u>superbugs</u>' that are resistant to most known antibiotics (e.g. MRSA) are becoming more common.

> If you're prescribed antibiotics, it's important to finish the whole course — this helps to prevent the spread of antibiotic resistance. Doctors only prescribing antibiotics when they're really needed helps too.

Some mutations make you find revising enjoyable...

Hopefully now you understand a bit more about the dangers of things like smoking and sunbeds — they can <u>mutate</u> your DNA, and this <u>usually</u> has a harmful effect on an organism. But don't forget that some mutations <u>benefit</u> an organism — <u>antibiotic resistance</u> is a good mutation for <u>bacteria</u>, but pretty rubbish for sick people...

Paper 2

Revision Summary for Section 7

There's a lot to remember in this section, with quite a variety of topics — but the 'R' word pretty much sums it all up. (Reproduction.) So now all you've got to do is the other 'R' word. (Revise.) But don't worry — I've made another load of questions to help you. Work your way through them and then, if you get any wrong, go back and learn those bits again. Can't say fairer than that.

1) What is a gene?

2) What does diploid mean? What is the diploid number for a human body cell?

3) Name the four different bases found in DNA. How do they pair up?

4) a) Name the type of cell division used in asexual reproduction.
   b) Apart from asexual reproduction, what else is this type of cell division used for?

5) Explain why sexual reproduction results in offspring that are genetically different from either parent.

6) Name the type of cell division that creates gametes. Where does it take place in humans?

7) Name the male and female reproductive parts of a flower.

8) What is pollination?

9) Give three differences between plants that are pollinated by insects and ones that are wind-pollinated.

10) What is fertilisation? How does the pollen get from the stigma to the ovary?

11) What conditions are needed for seed germination?

12) Give an example of a plant that reproduces asexually and briefly describe how it happens.

13) Describe how to make plant clones from cuttings.

14) Where are sperm made? Where are ova made?

15) What secondary sexual characteristics does testosterone trigger in males? And oestrogen in females?

16) Sketch a timeline of the 28-day menstrual cycle.
    Label the four stages of the cycle and show when the ovum is released.

17) What roles do oestrogen and progesterone play in the menstrual cycle?

18) What is the function of the amniotic fluid in pregnancy?

19) What does it mean if you are homozygous for a particular trait?

20) What are codominant alleles?

21)* Draw a genetic diagram for a cross between a man who has blue eyes (bb) and a woman who has green eyes (Bb). The gene for blue eyes (b) is recessive.
    What is the probability of the couple having a blue-eyed child?

22) Which two chromosomes determine whether you are male or female?

23) Draw a genetic diagram showing that there's an equal chance of a baby being a boy or a girl.

24) List four features of animals which aren't affected at all by their environment, and three which are.

25) Write down a brief summary of the theory of evolution.

26) Explain what is meant by natural selection.

27) What is a mutation?

28) Give an example of how a genetic mutation could be: a) harmful, b) beneficial.

29) What is a 'superbug'?

* Answer on p.92

Section 7 — Reproduction and Inheritance

Ecosystems

This is where the <u>fun</u> starts. Studying <u>ecology</u> gives you the chance to <u>rummage around</u> in bushes, get your hands <u>dirty</u> and look at some <u>real organisms</u>, living in the <u>wild</u>. Hold on to your hats folks...

You Need to Learn Some Definitions to get you Started

Habitat	— The <u>place</u> where an organism <u>lives</u>, e.g. a rocky shore or a field.
Population	— <u>All</u> the organisms of <u>one species</u> in a <u>habitat</u>.
Community	— All the <u>different species</u> in a habitat.
Ecosystem	— All the <u>organisms</u> living in a <u>particular area</u> and all the <u>non-living</u> (abiotic) <u>conditions</u>, e.g. temperature, climate, soil-type.

You Can Estimate Population Sizes in Different Areas Using a Quadrat

A <u>quadrat</u> is a square frame enclosing a known area, e.g. 1 m². You just place it on the ground, and look at what's inside it. To estimate <u>population size</u> in an area:

1) Place a <u>1 m² quadrat</u> on the ground at a <u>random point</u> within the area you're investigating.

2) <u>Count</u> all the organisms within the quadrat.

3) <u>Multiply</u> the number of organisms by the <u>total area</u> (in m²) of the habitat.

You can then do this again in another area and compare the population sizes.

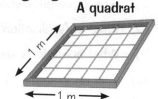
A quadrat
1 m
1 m

Samples should be random to avoid bias, e.g. if you were investigating a field you could pick random sample sites by dividing the field into a grid and using a random number generator to select coordinates.

Two Important Points About This Kind of Counting Method...

1) The sample may not be <u>representative</u> of the population, i.e. what you find in your particular sample might be different from what you'd have found if you'd looked at other bits of the habitat.

2) The <u>sample size</u> affects the <u>accuracy</u> of the estimate — the bigger your sample, the more accurate your estimate of the total population is likely to be. So it's better to use the quadrat at <u>several points</u>, get an <u>average</u> value for the number of organisms in a 1 m² quadrat, then multiply that by the total area.

You Can Use Quadrats to Investigate the Distribution of Organisms too

You can use quadrats to help find out how organisms (like plants) are <u>distributed</u> across their habitat — e.g. how species <u>change</u> from a hedge towards the middle of a field. The quadrats are laid out along a <u>line</u> called a <u>transect</u>.

Here's what to do:

1) <u>Mark out a line</u> in the area you want to study e.g. from the hedge to the middle of the field.

2) Then <u>collect data</u> along the line using <u>quadrats</u> placed <u>next to</u> each other.

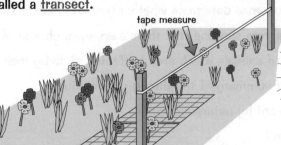
tape measure
quadrat

Transects can be used in any ecosystem, not just fields. For example, along a beach.

Drat, drat, and double drat — my favourite use of quadrats...

A <u>point quadrat</u> is another sort of quadrat that's used sometimes for studying plant populations. It looks kind of a like a test-tube rack. You poke a metal pin down each hole in the rack and record what species it touches, then move the rack along a bit. This makes it very precise, but also very faffy. Personally, I prefer frames.

Pyramids of Number, Biomass and Energy

OK, I'll level with you. This isn't the most <u>interesting</u> page in the world, but hey — life's like that. At least you're not being eaten by a load of <u>rabbits</u>...

Food Chains **Show What's Eaten by What** *in an Ecosystem*

1) <u>Food chains</u> always start with a <u>producer</u>, e.g. a plant. Producers <u>make</u> (produce) <u>their own food</u> using energy from the Sun.

2) Producers are eaten by <u>primary consumers</u>. Primary consumers are then eaten by <u>secondary consumers</u> and secondary consumers are eaten by <u>tertiary consumers</u>.

3) All these organisms eventually die and get eaten by <u>decomposers</u>, e.g. bacteria. Decomposers <u>break down</u> (decompose) <u>dead material</u> and <u>waste</u>.

4) Each <u>stage</u> (e.g. producers, primary consumers) is called a <u>trophic level</u>.

> <u>Consumers</u> are organisms that <u>eat</u> other organisms. '<u>Primary</u>' means '<u>first</u>', so primary consumers are the first consumers in a food chain. <u>Secondary</u> consumers are <u>second</u> and <u>tertiary</u> consumers are <u>third</u>.

Here's an <u>example</u> of a food chain:

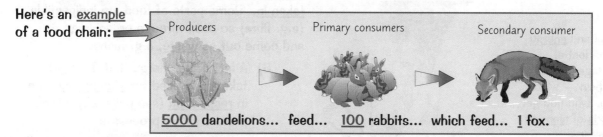

Producers   Primary consumers   Secondary consumer

<u>5000</u> dandelions... feed... <u>100</u> rabbits... which feed... <u>1</u> fox.

You Need to Understand Pyramids of Numbers

Here's a <u>pyramid of numbers</u> for the food chain above.

1) Each bar on a pyramid of numbers shows the <u>number of organisms</u> at that stage of the food chain.

2) So the '<u>dandelions</u>' bar on this pyramid would need to be <u>longer</u> than the '<u>rabbits</u>' bar, which in turn should be <u>longer</u> than the '<u>fox</u>' bar.

Secondary consumer → 1 fox
Primary consumers → 100 rabbits
Producers → 5000 dandelions

3) <u>Dandelions</u> go at the <u>bottom</u> because they're at the bottom of the food chain.

4) This is a <u>typical pyramid of numbers</u>, where every time you go up a <u>trophic level</u>, the number of organisms goes <u>down</u>. This is because it takes a <u>lot</u> of food from the level below to keep one animal alive.

5) There are cases where a number pyramid is <u>not a pyramid at all</u>. For example 1 fox may feed 500 fleas.

You Have to Understand Pyramids of Biomass *Too*

1) Each bar on a <u>pyramid of biomass</u> shows the <u>mass of living material</u> at that stage of the food chain — basically how much all the organisms at each level would '<u>weigh</u>' if you put them <u>all together</u>.

2) So the one fox would have a <u>big biomass</u> and the <u>hundreds of fleas</u> would have a <u>very small biomass</u>. Biomass pyramids are <u>practically always the right shape</u>.

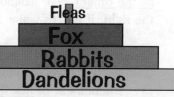

Fleas
Fox
Rabbits
Dandelions

Pyramids of Energy Transfer *Are Always* Pyramid-Shaped

1) <u>Pyramids of energy</u> show the <u>energy</u> transferred to each trophic level in a food chain. E.g. when a rabbit eats dandelions it gets energy, which the dandelions got from the Sun.

2) Pyramids of energy transfer are <u>always the right shape</u> — a nice, regular pyramid.

Constructing pyramids is a breeze — just ask the Egyptians...

If you have to <u>construct</u> a pyramid, check it's to scale. E.g. if one square = 10 units, 5 units of fox biomass would be half a square, but 500 units of dandelion biomass would need a 50 square block (e.g. 5 × 10 squares).

Energy Transfer and Food Webs

Some organisms get their <u>energy</u> from the Sun and some get it from other organisms, and it's all very friendly. Yeah right.

Energy *is* Transferred *Along a* Food Chain

1) Energy from the <u>Sun</u> is the source of energy for nearly <u>all</u> life on Earth.

2) <u>Plants</u> use light energy from the Sun to make <u>food</u> during photosynthesis. This energy then works its way through the food chain as animals eat the plants and each other.

3) Not all the energy that's available to the organisms in a trophic level is passed on to the next trophic level — around <u>90%</u> of the energy is <u>lost</u> in various ways.

4) Some parts of food, e.g. roots or bones, <u>aren't eaten</u> by organisms so the energy isn't <u>taken in</u>. Some parts of food are <u>indigestible</u> (e.g. fibre) so pass through organisms and come out as <u>waste</u>, e.g. faeces.

5) A lot of the energy that does get taken in is used for <u>staying alive</u>, i.e. in <u>respiration</u> (see page 28), which powers all life processes.

6) Most of this energy is eventually <u>lost</u> to the surroundings as <u>heat</u>.

7) Only around <u>10%</u> of the total energy available becomes <u>biomass</u>, i.e. it's <u>stored</u> or used for <u>growth</u>.

8) This is the <u>energy</u> that's <u>transferred</u> from one trophic level to the next.

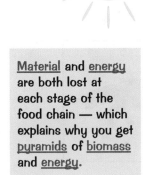

Material and <u>energy</u> are both lost at each stage of the food chain — which explains why you get <u>pyramids</u> of <u>biomass</u> and <u>energy</u>.

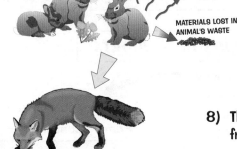

HEAT LOSS

MATERIALS LOST IN ANIMAL'S WASTE

Food Webs *Show How* Food Chains *are* Linked

1) There are many different species within an environment — which means <u>lots of different</u> possible <u>food chains</u>. You can draw a <u>food web</u> to show them.

2) All the species in a food web are <u>interdependent</u>, which means if one species changes, it <u>affects all the others</u>. For example, in the food web on the right, if lots of water spiders died, then:

- There would be <u>less food</u> for the <u>frogs</u>, so their numbers might <u>decrease</u>.
- The number of <u>mayfly larvae</u> might <u>increase</u> since the water spiders wouldn't be eating them.
- The <u>diving beetles</u> wouldn't be <u>competing</u> with the water spiders for food, so their numbers might <u>increase</u>.

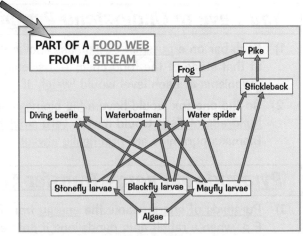

PART OF A <u>FOOD WEB</u> FROM A <u>STREAM</u>

Pike

Frog

Stickleback

Diving beetle | Waterboatman | Water spider

Stonefly larvae | Blackfly larvae | Mayfly larvae

Algae

Food webs — nothing to do with ordering pizza online, I'm afraid...

Food webs are <u>handy</u> for looking at <u>relationships</u> between individual species. Unfortunately you hardly ever see <u>simple</u> food webs in the real world — they're normally <u>tangled</u> together and <u>interlinked</u> like a bowl of <u>spaghetti</u>.

The Water Cycle and The Carbon Cycle

There's a bit of cycling to do here. Don't worry though — there aren't any actual hills to climb...

The Water Cycle Means Water is Endlessly Recycled

The water here on planet Earth is constantly recycled. Strange but true...

1) Heat from the Sun makes water evaporate from the land and sea, turning it into water vapour. Water also evaporates from plants — this is known as transpiration (see p.25).

2) The warm water vapour is carried upwards (as warm air rises). When it gets higher up it cools and condenses to form clouds.

3) Water falls from the clouds as precipitation (usually rain, but sometimes snow or hail) and is returned to the land and sea.

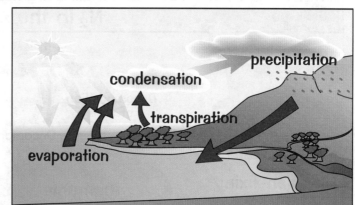

The Carbon Cycle Shows How Carbon is Recycled

Carbon is an important element in the materials that living things are made from. But there's only a fixed amount of carbon in the world. This means it's constantly recycled:

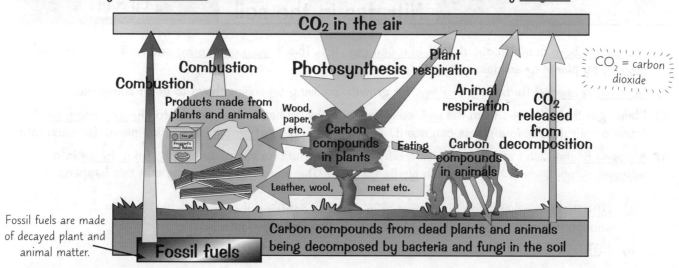

This diagram isn't half as bad as it looks. Learn these important points:

1) There's only one arrow going down. The whole thing is 'powered' by photosynthesis. Green plants use the carbon from CO_2 in the air to make carbohydrates, fats and proteins.

2) Eating passes the carbon compounds in the plant along to animals in a food chain or web.

3) Both plant and animal respiration while the organisms are alive releases CO_2 back into the air.

4) Plants and animals eventually die and decompose, or are killed and turned into useful products.

5) When plants and animals decompose they're broken down by bacteria and fungi. These decomposers release CO_2 back into the air by respiration, as they break down the material.

6) Some useful plant and animal products, e.g. wood and fossil fuels, are burned (combustion). This also releases CO_2 back into the air.

Come on out, it's only a little carbon cycle, it can't hurt you...

Carbon is a very important element for living things. Carbon molecules are found in plants, animals, your petrol tank and on your burnt toast. They get cycled round and the concentration of them in the atmosphere fluctuates up and down. They also do the hokey-cokey and they turn around. That's what they're all about.

The Nitrogen Cycle

Nitrogen, just like carbon, is constantly being recycled. So the nitrogen in your proteins might once have been in the air. And before that it might have been in a plant. Or even in some horse wee. Nice.

Nitrogen is Also Recycled in the Nitrogen Cycle

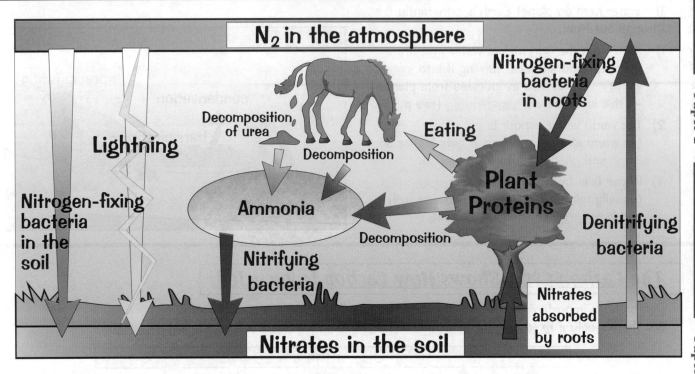

1) The atmosphere contains about 78% nitrogen gas, N_2. This is very unreactive and so it can't be used directly by plants or animals.

2) Nitrogen is needed for making proteins for growth, so living organisms have to get it somehow.

3) Plants get their nitrogen from the soil, so nitrogen in the air has to be turned into nitrogen compounds (such as nitrates) before plants can use it. Animals can only get proteins by eating plants (or each other).

4) Nitrogen fixation isn't an obsession with nitrogen — it's the process of turning N_2 from the air into nitrogen compounds in the soil which plants can use. There are two main ways that this happens:

   a) LIGHTNING — there's so much energy in a bolt of lightning that it's enough to make nitrogen react with oxygen in the air to give nitrates.

   b) NITROGEN-FIXING BACTERIA in roots and soil (see below).

5) There are four different types of bacteria involved in the nitrogen cycle:

   a) DECOMPOSERS — break down proteins (in rotting plants and animals) and urea (in animal waste) and turn them into ammonia (a nitrogen compound).

   b) NITRIFYING BACTERIA — turn ammonia in decaying matter into nitrates.

   c) NITROGEN-FIXING BACTERIA — turn atmospheric N_2 into nitrogen compounds that plants can use.

   d) DENITRIFYING BACTERIA — turn nitrates back into N_2 gas. This is of no benefit to living organisms.

   Some of these bacteria live in the soil and some of them live in nodules on plant roots.

It's the cyyyycle of liiiiife...

Nitrogen is vital to living things, because it's found in proteins, which are needed for things like enzymes. It's also found in DNA, so you can see it's pretty important. Make sure you learn this page.

Air Pollution

Water, carbon and nitrogen all pass through the air as an essential part of natural cycles. But <u>air pollutants</u> can cause lots of <u>problems</u> when they're released into the atmosphere — especially when <u>we</u> put them there.

Carbon Monoxide is Poisonous

1) When <u>fossil fuels</u> are burnt <u>without enough air supply</u> they produce the gas <u>carbon monoxide</u> (CO).

2) It's a <u>poisonous</u> gas. If it <u>combines</u> with <u>red blood cells</u>, it prevents them from carrying oxygen.

3) Carbon monoxide's mostly released in <u>car emissions</u>. Most <u>modern cars</u> are fitted with <u>catalytic converters</u> that turn the <u>carbon monoxide</u> into carbon dioxide, decreasing the amount of CO that's released into the atmosphere.

Acid Rain is Caused by Sulfur Dioxide

1) <u>Burning fossil fuels</u> releases harmful gases like <u>CO_2</u> (a greenhouse gas, see next page) and <u>sulfur dioxide</u> (SO_2).

2) The <u>sulfur dioxide</u> comes from <u>sulfur impurities</u> in the <u>fossil fuels</u>.

3) When this gas <u>mixes</u> with <u>rain clouds</u> it forms dilute <u>sulfuric acid</u>.

4) This then falls as <u>acid rain</u>.

5) <u>Internal combustion engines</u> in cars and <u>power stations</u> are the <u>main causes</u> of acid rain.

> Acid rain is also caused by nitrogen oxides that are produced by burning fossil fuels.

sulfur dioxide — Clean Cloud — Acid Cloud — Acid Rain

Acid Rain Kills Fish and Trees

1) Acid rain can cause a <u>lake</u> to become more <u>acidic</u>. This has a <u>severe effect</u> on the lake's <u>ecosystem</u>. Many organisms are <u>sensitive</u> to <u>changes in pH</u> and <u>can't survive</u> in more acidic conditions. Many plants and animals die.

2) Acid rain can kill <u>trees</u>. The acid <u>damages leaves</u> and releases <u>toxic substances</u> from the soil, making it <u>hard</u> for the trees to <u>take up nutrients</u>.

It's raining, it's pouring — quick, cover the rhododendron...

Exam questions on this topic might ask you to <u>describe</u> the effects of air pollution, mini-essay style. Or they may give you a graph or table to interpret — in which case you'll have to <u>apply your knowledge</u>. Either way, you'll need to <u>learn</u> all the facts on this page. Try covering up the page and jotting down everything you can remember.

The Greenhouse Effect

The greenhouse effect is always in the news. We need it, since it makes Earth a suitable temperature for living on. But unfortunately it's starting to trap more heat than is necessary.

Greenhouse Gases Trap Heat from the Sun

1) The temperature of the Earth is a balance between the heat it gets from the Sun and the heat it radiates back out into space.

2) Gases in the atmosphere absorb most of the heat that would normally be radiated out into space, and re-radiate it in all directions (including back towards the Earth).

3) If this didn't happen, then at night there'd be nothing to keep any heat in, and we'd quickly get very cold indeed.

4) There are several different gases in the atmosphere that help keep the heat in. They're called "greenhouse gases" (oddly enough) and they include water vapour, carbon dioxide and methane.

5) Human beings are increasing the amount of carbon dioxide in the atmosphere (see below). We're also increasing levels of other gases that can act as greenhouse gases, e.g. CFCs and nitrous oxide (again, see below). This has enhanced the greenhouse effect.

6) As a result of all this, the Earth is heating up — this is global warming. Global warming is a type of climate change and causes other types of climate change, e.g. changing rainfall patterns. Climate change could lead to things like changing crop growth patterns or flooding due to the polar ice caps melting.

This is what happens in a greenhouse. The Sun shines in, and the glass helps keeps some of the heat in.

Human Activity Produces Lots of Greenhouse Gases

CARBON DIOXIDE

1) Humans release carbon dioxide into the atmosphere all the time as part of our everyday lives — in car exhausts, industrial processes, as we burn fossil fuels etc.

2) People around the world are also cutting down large areas of forest (deforestation) for timber and to clear land for farming — and this activity affects the level of carbon dioxide in the atmosphere (see next page).

METHANE

1) Methane gas is also produced naturally from various sources, e.g. rotting plants in marshland.

2) However, two 'man-made' sources of methane are on the increase: rice growing and cattle rearing — it's the cows' "pumping" that's the problem, believe it or not.

NITROUS OXIDE

1) Nitrous oxide is released naturally by bacteria in soils and the ocean.

2) A lot more is released from soils after fertiliser is used.

3) It's also released from vehicle engines and industry.

CFCs

1) CFCs are man-made chemicals that were once used in aerosol sprays (e.g. deodorant) and fridges. They're really powerful greenhouse gases.

2) Most countries have agreed not to produce them any more because they also damage the ozone layer, which prevents UV radiation from reaching the Earth.

3) But some CFCs still remain and get released, e.g. by leaks from old fridges.

Methane is a stinky problem but an important one...

Global warming is rarely out of the news. There's a consensus among scientists that it's happening and that human activity has caused most of the recent warming. But, they don't know exactly what the effects will be.

Water Pollution and Deforestation

I'm sorry to bring so much <u>gloom</u> in such a short space, but here are a couple more environmental problems for you to learn about — <u>river pollution</u> by fertiliser or sewage, and the effects of <u>chopping down</u> too many trees.

Fertilisers can Leach into Water and Cause Eutrophication

You might think <u>fertiliser</u> would be a good thing for the environment because it makes plants grow faster. Unfortunately it causes <u>big problems</u> when it ends up in <u>lakes</u> and <u>rivers</u> — here's how...

1) <u>Nitrates</u> and <u>phosphates</u> are put onto fields as <u>mineral fertilisers</u>.

2) If <u>too much fertiliser</u> is applied and it <u>rains</u> afterwards, nitrates are easily <u>leached</u> (washed through the soil) into rivers and lakes.

3) The result is <u>eutrophication</u>, which can cause serious damage to rivers and lakes:

2) The extra nutrients cause <u>algae</u> to <u>grow fast</u> and <u>block out the light</u>.

3) <u>Plants can't photosynthesise</u> due to lack of light and <u>start to die</u>.

1) <u>Fertilisers</u> enter the water, adding <u>extra nutrients</u> (nitrates and phosphates).

4) With more food available, microorganisms that feed on dead plants <u>increase in number</u> and <u>deplete</u> (use up) <u>all the oxygen</u> in the water.

5) Organisms that need oxygen (e.g. <u>fish</u>) <u>die</u>.

Paper 2

4) Another cause of <u>eutrophication</u> is pollution by <u>sewage</u>. Sewage contains lots of <u>phosphates</u> from <u>detergents</u>, e.g. washing powder. It also contains <u>nitrates</u> from urine and faeces.

5) These extra nutrients cause eutrophication in the <u>same way that fertilisers do</u>.

Deforestation Affects The Soil, Water Cycle and Carbon Cycle

Deforestation is bad. Chop down all the trees, and the animals and insects that lived there will disappear too. But there are some other <u>nasty effects</u> that you need to know about...

LEACHING

- Trees <u>take up nutrients</u> from the soil <u>before</u> they can be <u>washed away</u> (leached) by rain, but return them to the soil when leaves die.
- When trees are removed nutrients get <u>leached away</u>, but <u>don't</u> get <u>replaced</u>, leaving <u>infertile soil</u>.

SOIL EROSION

- Tree roots <u>hold the soil together</u>.
- When trees are <u>removed</u>, soil can be <u>washed away</u> by the rain (<u>eroded</u>) leaving <u>infertile</u> ground.

DISTURBING THE WATER CYCLE

- Trees <u>stop rainwater</u> reaching rivers too quickly.
- When they're cut down, rainwater can run <u>straight into rivers</u> — this can lead to <u>flooding</u>.
- <u>Transpiration</u> from trees releases some of the rainwater <u>back into</u> the <u>atmosphere</u> (see page 69).
- When they're cut down this can make the <u>local climate drier</u>.

DISTURBING THE BALANCE OF CARBON DIOXIDE AND OXYGEN

- Forests take up CO_2 by <u>photosynthesis</u>, <u>store</u> it in <u>wood</u>, and slowly release it when they <u>decompose</u> (microorganisms feeding on bits of <u>dead wood</u> release CO_2 as a waste product of <u>respiration</u>).
- When trees are cut down and <u>burnt</u>, the stored carbon is <u>released</u> at once as CO_2. This contributes to <u>global warming</u> (see p.72).
- Fewer trees in the forest also means that <u>less photosynthesis</u> takes place, releasing <u>less oxygen</u>. This causes the oxygen level in the atmosphere to <u>drop</u>.

Bet you never knew trees were so useful...

Trees remove CO_2 from the atmosphere as they grow — but once they die and decompose, the CO_2 is released. But if the carbon gets stored in wood products, it is <u>permanently</u> removed from the atmosphere.

Revision Summary for Section 8

Here goes, folks — another beautiful page of revision questions to keep you at your desk studying hard until your parents have gone out and you can finally nip downstairs to watch TV. Think twice though before you reach for that remote control. These questions are actually pretty good — certainly more entertaining than 'Train Your Husband Like He's a Dog' or 'Celebrities Dance Around'. Question 14 is almost as good as an episode of 'Supernanny'. Question 4 is the corker though — like a reunion episode of 'Friends' but a lot funnier. Give the questions a go. Oh go on.

1) Define the following:
   a) a habitat
   b) a population
   c) an ecosystem

2) How could you estimate a population size in a habitat using a quadrat?
   Give two reasons why your results might not be 100% accurate.

3) How could you investigate the distribution of organisms within an area using quadrats?

4) What's a producer? What's a secondary consumer?

5) Give an example of a decomposer.

6) Explain why pyramids of number are not always pyramid-shaped.

7) What is the source of all the energy in a typical food chain?

8) Approximately how much energy is passed on to the next trophic level?

9) Give two reasons why energy is lost between trophic levels.

10) What does a food web show?

11) Draw a sketch of the water cycle. Include evaporation, transpiration, condensation and precipitation. What do those words mean?

12) How does carbon enter the carbon cycle from the air?

13) Give two ways that carbon can enter the air from dead plants and animals.

14) What role do decomposers play in the nitrogen cycle?

15) What role do nitrogen-fixing bacteria play in the nitrogen cycle?

16) Name a gas that causes acid rain. How is it produced?

17) How does acid rain affect lakes and trees?

18) How does the greenhouse effect work?

19) What is the effect of increasing the concentration of greenhouse gases in the atmosphere?

20) Name four greenhouse gases that humans make. How are they produced?

21) What is eutrophication? How does it kill fish?

22) Describe four effects of deforestation.

Section 8 — Ecology and the Environment

Increasing Crop Yields

A plant's rate of photosynthesis is affected by the amount of light, the amount of carbon dioxide (CO_2) and the temperature (see page 20). Since plants have to photosynthesise in order to make food for themselves and grow, these three factors need to be carefully controlled in order to maximise crop yield.

You Can Artificially Create the Ideal Conditions for Photosynthesis

Photosynthesis can be helped along by artificially creating the ideal conditions in glasshouses (big greenhouses to you and me) or polytunnels (big tube-like structures made from polythene).

1) Keeping plants enclosed in a glasshouse makes it easier to keep them free from pests and diseases.

2) Commercial farmers often supply artificial light after the Sun goes down to give their plants more time to photosynthesise.

3) Glasshouses trap the Sun's heat to keep the plants warm. In winter, a farmer might also use a heater to help keep the temperature at the ideal level.

4) Farmers can also increase the level of carbon dioxide in glasshouses, e.g. by using a paraffin heater to heat the place. As the paraffin burns, it makes carbon dioxide as a by-product.

5) By increasing the temperature and CO_2 concentration, as well as the amount of light available, a farmer can increase the rate of photosynthesis for his or her plants. This means the plants will grow faster and bigger — and crop yields will be higher.

Fertilisers Are Used to Ensure the Crops Have Enough Nutrients

1) Plants need certain elements, e.g. nitrogen, potassium and phosphorus, so they can make important compounds like proteins.

2) If plants don't get enough of these elements, their growth and life processes are affected.

3) Sometimes these elements are missing from the soil because they've been used up by a previous crop.

4) Farmers use fertilisers to replace these missing elements or provide more of them. This helps to increase the crop yield.

Pest Control Stops Pests Eating Crops

1) Pests include microorganisms, insects and mammals (e.g. rats). Pests that feed on crops are killed using various methods of pest control. This means fewer plants are damaged or destroyed, increasing crop yield.

2) Pesticides are a form of chemical pest control. They're often poisonous to humans, so they must be used carefully to keep the amount of pesticide in food below a safe level. Some pesticides also harm other wildlife.

3) Biological control is an alternative to using pesticides. It means using other organisms to reduce the numbers of pests, either by encouraging wild organisms or adding new ones.

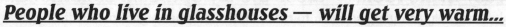

4) The helpful organisms could be predators (e.g. ladybirds eat aphids), parasites (e.g. some flies lay their eggs on slugs, eventually killing them), or disease-causing (e.g. bacteria that affect caterpillars).

5) Biological control can have a longer-lasting effect than spraying pesticides, and be less harmful to wildlife. But introducing new organisms can cause problems — e.g. cane toads were introduced to Australia to eat beetles, but they are now a major pest themselves because they poison the native species that eat them.

People who live in glasshouses — will get very warm...

Right. Now you know exactly what to do to increase crop yields. Excellent. With all this new-found knowledge you could take over the world — or at least help Gran with her veggie patch...

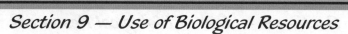

Bacteria and Making Yoghurt

Lots of microorganisms are used to produce food, including <u>bacteria</u>. You need to know how <u>yoghurt</u> is produced, and how giant <u>fermenters</u> are used for industrial-scale production of microbial products.

Bacteria Ferment Milk to Produce Yoghurt

<u>Fermentation</u> is when <u>microorganisms</u> break sugars down to release energy — usually by <u>anaerobic respiration</u>. <u>Yoghurt</u> is basically <u>fermented milk</u>. Here's how it's made...

1) The <u>equipment</u> is <u>sterilised</u> to kill off any unwanted microorganisms.

2) The milk is <u>pasteurised</u> (heated up to 72 °C for 15 seconds) — again to kill any harmful microorganisms. Then the milk's <u>cooled</u>.

3) *Lactobacillus* bacteria are added, and the mixture is <u>incubated</u> (heated to about 40 °C) in a vessel called a <u>fermenter</u> (see below).

4) The bacteria ferment the <u>lactose sugar</u> in the milk to form <u>lactic acid</u>.

5) Lactic acid causes the milk to <u>clot</u>, and <u>solidify</u> into <u>yoghurt</u>.

6) Finally, <u>flavours</u> (e.g. fruit) and <u>colours</u> are sometimes added and the yoghurt is <u>packaged</u>.

Microorganisms are Grown in Fermenters

1) <u>Microorganisms</u> (like bacteria) can be used to make really <u>useful stuff</u>, e.g. penicillin or insulin (see p.80).

2) <u>In industry</u>, microorganisms are grown in large containers called <u>fermenters</u>. The fermenter is full of liquid '<u>culture medium</u>' in which microorganisms can grow and reproduce.

3) The conditions inside the fermentation vessels are kept at the <u>optimum</u> (best) levels <u>for growth</u> — this means the <u>yield</u> of <u>products</u> from the microorganisms can be <u>as big as possible</u>.

Here's a bit about how fermenters work:

<u>Nutrients</u> needed by the mircoorganisms for <u>growth</u> are provided in the liquid <u>culture medium</u>.

The <u>pH</u> is monitored and kept at the <u>optimum level</u> for the microorganisms' <u>enzymes</u> to work <u>efficiently</u>. This keeps the <u>rate of reaction</u> and product yield as high as possible.

The <u>temperature</u> is also monitored and kept at an <u>optimum level</u>. A <u>water-cooled</u> jacket makes sure it doesn't get <u>so hot</u> that the enzymes <u>denature</u>.

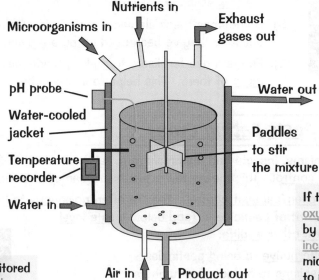

Nutrients in
Microorganisms in
Exhaust gases out
pH probe
Water out
Water-cooled jacket
Paddles to stir the mixture
Temperature recorder
Water in
Air in
Product out

Microorganisms are kept in <u>contact</u> with <u>fresh medium</u> by <u>paddles</u> that <u>circulate</u> (or <u>agitate</u>) the medium around the vessel. This <u>increases</u> the product yield because microorganisms can <u>always access</u> the <u>nutrients</u> needed for <u>growth</u>.

If the microorganisms need <u>oxygen</u> for <u>respiration</u>, it's added by pumping in sterile air. This <u>increases</u> the product yield because microorganisms can always <u>respire</u> to provide the <u>energy</u> for <u>growth</u>.

Vessels are <u>sterilised</u> between uses with <u>superheated steam</u> that kills <u>unwanted microbes</u>. Having <u>aseptic</u> conditions <u>increases</u> the product yield because the microorganisms <u>aren't competing</u> with other organisms. It also means that the product doesn't get <u>contaminated</u>.

Pizza, TV and a nice cosy living room — those are my optimum conditions...

Microorganisms are <u>really useful</u> — not only can you use them to make stuff that other organisms can't, they'll happily grow in a <u>fermenter</u> whether it's hot or cold or <u>blowing a gale</u> outside. Microorganisms can also use <u>waste products</u> from agriculture and industry as food, which often makes using them <u>cheaper</u> than other methods.

Yeast and Making Beer

Yeast is a very useful <u>microorganism</u>.. When yeast respires <u>aerobically</u> (in the presence of <u>oxygen</u>) it turns sugar into CO_2. But when there <u>isn't enough oxygen</u>, yeast respires <u>anaerobically</u>, turning sugar into CO_2 and <u>alcohol</u> — we use anaerobically respiring yeast to make <u>beer</u>.

We Use Yeast for Brewing Beer

1 Firstly you need to get the <u>sugar out</u> of the grain:

> ~ Germination is when ~
> a seed starts to grow
> into a new plant.

1) Beer is made from <u>grain</u> — usually <u>barley</u>.

2) The barley grains are allowed to <u>germinate</u> for a few days, during which the <u>starch</u> in the grains is broken down into <u>sugar</u> by <u>enzymes</u>. Then the grains are <u>dried</u> in a kiln. This is called <u>malting</u>.

3) The malted grain is <u>mashed up</u> and water is added to produce a <u>sugary solution</u> with lots of bits in it. This is then sieved to remove the bits.

4) <u>Hops</u> are added to the mixture to give the beer its <u>bitter flavour</u>.

2 <u>Yeast</u> is <u>added</u> and the mixture is <u>incubated</u> (warmed up). The yeast <u>ferments</u> the <u>sugar</u> into <u>alcohol</u>. The fermenting vessels are designed to stop <u>unwanted microorganisms</u> and <u>air getting in</u>.

1) The <u>rising concentration of alcohol (ethanol)</u> in the fermentation mixture due to <u>anaerobic respiration</u> eventually starts to <u>kill</u> the <u>yeast</u>. As the yeast dies, fermentation <u>slows</u> down.

2) Different species of yeast can <u>tolerate different levels of alcohol</u>. Some species can be used to produce strong beer with a <u>high concentration</u> of alcohol.

3 The beer is <u>drawn off</u> through a tap.
Sometimes chemicals called <u>clarifying agents</u> are added to <u>remove particles</u> and make it <u>clearer</u>.

4 The <u>beer</u> is then <u>pasteurised</u> — <u>heated</u> to <u>kill any yeast</u> left in the beer and completely stop fermentation. Beer tastes better if it's unpasteurised and aged in the <u>right conditions</u>. But big breweries pasteurise it because there's a <u>risk</u> unpasteurised beer will <u>spoil</u> if it's not stored in the right conditions after it's sold. Finally the <u>beer</u> is <u>casked</u> ready for sale.

The Respiration Rate of Yeast Depends on Its Conditions

You can do experiments to investigate how the <u>rate of CO_2 production</u> by yeast changes under <u>different conditions</u>. Here's how to measure the effect of <u>changing temperature</u>:

1) Mix together some <u>sugar</u>, <u>yeast</u> and <u>distilled water</u>, then add the mixture to a <u>test tube</u>.

2) Attach a <u>bung</u> with a tube leading to a second test tube of <u>water</u>.

3) Place the tube containing the yeast mixture in a <u>water bath</u> at a <u>certain temperature</u>.

4) Leave the tube to warm up a bit and then <u>count how many bubbles</u> are produced in a given <u>period of time</u> (e.g. one minute). Use this to calculate the <u>rate</u> of CO_2 production (which gives an indication of <u>respiration rate</u>).

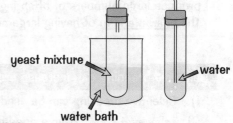

yeast mixture

water

water bath

5) Repeat the experiment with the water bath set at <u>different temperatures</u>.

6) Respiration is controlled by <u>enzymes</u> — so as temperature <u>increases</u>, so should the rate of respiration (up until the optimum temperature, see page 5 for more).

The example looks at how temperature affects the rate, but the basic idea would be the same whatever variable you were investigating. For example, you could vary the <u>concentration of sugar</u> (but keep the temperature of the water bath the same). You could also alter the experiment to give <u>more accurate</u> results by replacing the second tube with a <u>gas syringe</u> — you'd measure the <u>volume</u> of gas produced instead.

At yeast it's an easy page...

Remember, yeast is a <u>living organism</u>. Its respiration is carried out by <u>enzymes</u>, which are affected by things like <u>temperature</u> and <u>pH</u>. So if you change these conditions, CO_2 production will change too. Ace.

Section 9 — Use of Biological Resources

Selective Breeding

'Selective breeding' sounds like it has the potential to be a tricky topic, but it's actually dead simple. You take the best plants or animals and breed them together to get the best possible offspring. That's it.

Selective Breeding is Mating the Best Organisms to Get Good Offspring

Organisms are selectively bred to develop the best features, which are things like:

- Maximum yield of meat, milk, grain etc.
- Good health and disease resistance.
- In animals, other qualities like temperament, speed, fertility, good mothering skills, etc.
- In plants, other qualities like attractive flowers, nice smell, etc.

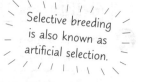

This is the basic process involved in selective breeding:

1) From your existing stock select the ones which have the best characteristics.
2) Breed them with each other.
3) Select the best of the offspring, and breed them together.
4) Continue this process over several generations, and the desirable trait gets stronger and stronger. In farming, this will give the farmer gradually better and better yields.

Selective breeding is also known as artificial selection.

Selective Breeding is Very Useful

Selective breeding can increase the productivity of cows

1) Cows can be selectively bred to produce offspring with, e.g. a high meat yield.
2) First, the animals with characteristics that will increase meat yield (e.g. the largest cows and bulls) are selected and bred together.
3) Next, the offspring with the best characteristics (e.g. the largest) are selected and bred together.
4) If this is continued over several generations, cows with very large meat yields can be produced.

Selective breeding can increase the number of offspring in sheep

Farmers can selectively breed sheep to increase the number of lambs born. Female sheep (ewes) who produce large numbers of offspring are bred with rams whose mothers had large numbers of offspring. The characteristic of having large numbers of offspring is passed on to the next generation.

Selective breeding can increase crop yield

1) Selective breeding can be used to combine two different desirable characteristics.
2) Tall wheat plants have a good grain yield but are easily damaged by wind and rain. Dwarf wheat plants can resist wind and rain but have a lower grain yield.
3) These two types of wheat plant were cross-bred, and the best resulting wheat plants were cross-bred again. This resulted in a new variety of wheat combining the good characteristics — dwarf wheat plants which could resist bad weather and had a high grain yield.

I'll have a roll, a loaf and a french stick — oh no, that's selective breading...

Selective breeding's not a new thing. People have been doing it for yonks. That's how we ended up with something like a poodle from a wolf. Somebody thought 'I really like this small, woolly, yappy wolf — I'll breed it with this other one'. And after thousands of generations, we got poodles. Hurrah.

Fish Farming

We're catching so many wild fish that, if we're not careful, there won't be many left.
A possible solution to this problem is <u>fish farms</u> — big <u>enclosures</u> or <u>tanks</u> where fish are raised for food.
<u>Fish farms</u> rear fish in a controlled way that's designed to produce <u>as many fish as possible</u>.

Fish Can Be Farmed In Cages In The Sea

<u>Salmon farming</u> in Scotland is a good example of this:

1) The fish are kept in <u>cages</u> in the <u>sea</u> to <u>stop them using as much energy</u> swimming about.

2) The cage also <u>protects</u> them from <u>interspecific predation</u> (being eaten by other animals like birds or seals).

3) They're fed a <u>diet</u> of food pellets that's <u>carefully controlled</u> to <u>maximise</u> the amount of energy they get. The better the <u>quality</u> the food is, the <u>quicker</u> and <u>bigger</u> the fish will grow. (Which is good for us as fish is a great <u>source of protein</u>.)

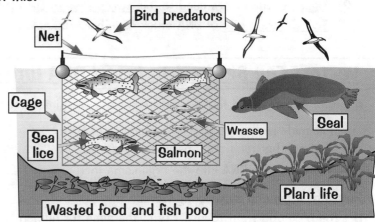

4) Young fish are reared in <u>special tanks</u> to ensure as many survive as possible.

5) It's important to keep younger fish <u>separate</u> from <u>bigger fish</u>, and to provide <u>regular food</u> — this makes sure that the big fish <u>don't eat the little ones</u>. This is <u>intraspecific predation</u> — where organisms eat individuals of the same species.

6) Fish kept in cages are more prone to <u>disease</u> and <u>parasites</u>. One pest is <u>sea lice</u>, which can be treated with <u>pesticides</u> which kill them. To <u>avoid pollution</u> from chemical pesticides, <u>biological pest control</u> (see p. 75) can be used instead, e.g. a small fish called a <u>wrasse</u> eats the lice off the backs of the salmon.

7) The fish can be <u>selectively bred</u> (see previous page) to produce <u>less aggressive</u>, <u>faster-growing</u> fish.

Fish Can Be Farmed In Tanks Too

Freshwater fish, e.g. <u>carp</u>, can be farmed in <u>ponds</u> or <u>indoors</u> in tanks where conditions can be <u>controlled</u>. This is especially useful for controlling the <u>water quality</u>.

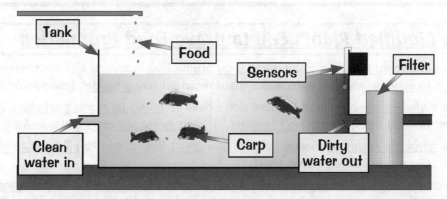

1) The <u>water</u> can be <u>monitored</u> to check the <u>temperature</u>, <u>pH</u> and <u>oxygen level</u> is OK.
2) It's easy to control <u>how much food</u> is supplied and give <u>exactly the right sort</u> of food.
3) The water can be <u>removed</u> and <u>filtered</u> to get rid of <u>waste food</u> and <u>fish poo</u>.
   This keeps the water <u>clean</u> for the fish and avoids <u>pollution</u> wherever the water ends up.

Two fish in a tank — one asks the other, "How do you drive this thing?"...

If you're thinking to yourself, "Why do we bother with all this faff? They're only fish" — think again. Fish are an excellent <u>source of protein</u> — which we all need to grow up big and strong. They're also pretty darn <u>tasty</u>.

Genetic Engineering

The basic idea of genetic engineering is to move <u>useful genes</u> from one organism's chromosomes into the cells of another. Although that sounds difficult, people have found <u>enzymes</u> and <u>vectors</u> (carriers) that can do it.

Enzymes *Can Be Used To Cut Up* DNA *or Join DNA Pieces* Together

1) <u>Restriction enzymes</u> recognise <u>specific sequences</u> of DNA and <u>cut the DNA</u> at these points.
2) <u>Ligase</u> enzymes are used to join <u>two pieces of DNA</u> together.
3) <u>Two different bits</u> of DNA stuck together are known as <u>recombinant DNA</u>.

Vectors *Can Be Used To* Insert DNA *Into* Other Organisms

A <u>vector</u> is something that's used to <u>transfer DNA</u> into a <u>cell</u>. There are two sorts — <u>plasmids</u> and <u>viruses</u>:

- Plasmids are <u>small</u>, <u>circular</u> molecules of DNA that can be <u>transferred</u> between <u>bacteria</u>.
- Viruses <u>insert</u> DNA into the organisms they <u>infect</u>.

Here's how genetic engineering works:

1) The <u>DNA</u> you want to <u>insert</u> (e.g. the gene for human insulin) is cut out with a <u>restriction enzyme</u>. The <u>vector DNA</u> is then cut open using the <u>same</u> restriction enzyme.

2) The vector DNA and the DNA you're inserting are <u>mixed together</u> with <u>ligase enzymes</u>.

3) The ligases <u>join</u> the two pieces of DNA together to produce <u>recombinant DNA</u>.

4) The recombinant DNA (i.e. the vector containing new DNA) is <u>inserted</u> into other cells, e.g. bacteria.

5) These cells can now <u>use the gene you inserted</u> to <u>make the protein</u> you want. E.g. <u>bacteria</u> containing the gene for <u>human insulin</u> can be grown in huge numbers in a fermenter (see page 76) to produce <u>insulin</u> for people with <u>diabetes</u>.

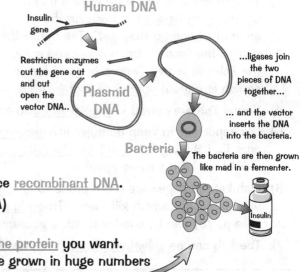

Human DNA

Insulin gene

Restriction enzymes cut the gene out and cut open the vector DNA..

Plasmid DNA

...ligases join the two pieces of DNA together...

... and the vector inserts the DNA into the bacteria.

Bacteria

The bacteria are then grown like mad in a fermenter.

Insulin

Paper 2

Bacteria that contain the gene for human insulin are <u>transgenic</u> — this means that they contain <u>genes transferred from another species</u>. You can get transgenic animals and plants too.

Genetically Modified Plants *Can* Improve *Food Production*

1) Crops can be <u>genetically modified</u> to increase <u>food production</u> in lots of different ways — one is to make them <u>resistant to insects</u>, another is to make them resistant to <u>herbicides</u> (chemicals that kill plants).

2) Making crops <u>insect-resistant</u> means farmers don't have to <u>spray as many pesticides</u> (see page 75) — so <u>wildlife</u> that doesn't eat the crop <u>isn't harmed</u>. It also <u>increases</u> crop <u>yield</u>, making more <u>food</u>.

3) Making crops <u>herbicide-resistant</u> means farmers can <u>spray</u> their crops to <u>kill weeds</u>, <u>without affecting</u> the <u>crop</u> itself. This can also increase crop yield.

4) There are concerns about growing genetically modified crops though. One is that <u>transplanted genes</u> may get out into the <u>environment</u>. For example, a herbicide resistance gene may be picked up by weeds, creating a new 'superweed' variety. Another concern is that genetically modified crops could adversely affect <u>food chains</u> — or even <u>human health</u>.

I say it's great.

5) Some people are against <u>genetic engineering</u> altogether — they <u>worry</u> that changing an organism's genes might create unforeseen <u>problems</u> — which could then get passed on to <u>future generations</u>.

If only there was a gene to make revision easier...

Ahhh, sitting in the sun, licking an <u>ice cream</u>, exams <u>all over</u>. That's where you'll be in a few months' time. After revising <u>this nasty stuff</u> that is. As genetic engineering advances, <u>more questions</u> will pop up about its implications. So it's a good idea to know <u>both sides</u> of the argument — <u>especially</u> for the exam.

Cloning

Clones are <u>genetically identical organisms</u>. They can be made <u>artificially</u>, which is <u>great</u> if you have just one organism with really <u>useful properties</u> — cloning it gives you <u>lots more</u>.

Micropropagation is Used to Clone Plants

Plants can be cloned from existing plants using a technique called <u>micropropagation</u> (tissue culture):

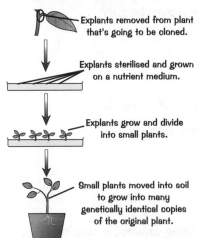

Explants removed from plant that's going to be cloned.

Explants sterilised and grown on a nutrient medium.

Explants grow and divide into small plants.

Small plants moved into soil to grow into many genetically identical copies of the original plant.

1) A plant with <u>desirable characteristics</u> (e.g. large fruit or pretty flowers) is selected to be <u>cloned</u>. Small pieces (called <u>explants</u>) are taken from the <u>tips of the stems</u> and the <u>side shoots</u> of this plant.

2) The explants are <u>sterilised</u> to kill any <u>microorganisms</u>.

3) The explants are then grown <u>in vitro</u> — this means that they're placed in a <u>petri dish</u> containing a <u>nutrient medium</u>. The medium has all the nutrients the explants need to grow. It also contains <u>growth hormones</u>.

4) Cells in the explants <u>divide</u> and <u>grow</u> into a <u>small plant</u>. If <u>large quantities</u> of plants are required (e.g. to sell), further explants can be taken from these small plants, and so on until <u>enough</u> small plants are produced.

5) The <u>small plants</u> are taken out of the medium, <u>planted in soil</u> and put into <u>glasshouses</u> — they'll develop into plants that are <u>genetically identical</u> to the <u>original plant</u> — so they share the <u>same characteristics</u>.

Cloning an Adult Mammal is Done by Transplanting a Cell Nucleus

The <u>first mammal</u> to be successfully cloned from an <u>adult cell</u> was a sheep called "Dolly" in 1996. This is the method that was used to produce Dolly:

Egg cell

Adult body cell

Nucleus removed

Nucleus removed

Enucleated egg cell

+

Embryo

Implanted into surrogate mother

1) The <u>nucleus</u> of a sheep's <u>egg cell</u> was removed, creating an <u>enucleated cell</u> (i.e. a cell without a nucleus).

2) A <u>diploid</u> nucleus (with a full set of paired chromosomes — see page 51) was <u>inserted</u> in its place. This was a nucleus from a mature udder cell of a <u>different sheep</u>.

3) The cell was <u>stimulated</u> (by an electric shock) so that it started <u>dividing by mitosis</u>, as if it was a normal <u>fertilised egg</u>.

4) The dividing cell was <u>implanted</u> into the <u>uterus</u> of another sheep to develop until it was ready to be born.

5) The result was <u>Dolly</u>, a <u>clone</u> of the sheep that the <u>udder cell</u> came from.

<u>Other animals</u> can also be cloned using this method.

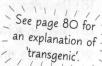

There Are Advantages and Disadvantages to Cloning

See page 80 for an explanation of 'transgenic'.

There are many possible <u>uses</u> for cloned <u>transgenic</u> animals:

1) Animals that can produce <u>medicines</u> in their <u>milk</u> could be cloned. Researchers have managed to transfer <u>human genes</u> that produce <u>useful proteins</u> into <u>sheep</u> and <u>cows</u>, for example <u>human antibodies</u> used in therapy for illnesses like <u>arthritis</u>, some types of <u>cancer</u> and <u>multiple sclerosis</u>.

2) Animals (probably pigs) that have organs suitable for <u>organ transplantation</u> into humans could be developed by <u>genetic engineering</u> and then <u>cloned</u> in the same way.

3) The main <u>benefits</u> of cloning are that the useful genetic characteristics are <u>always passed on</u> — this doesn't always happen with <u>breeding</u>. Farmers also don't have to <u>wait</u> until the <u>breeding season</u>, and <u>infertile</u> animals can be cloned.

4) But there are <u>risks</u> too. There's evidence that cloned animals might <u>not</u> be as <u>healthy</u> as normal ones. Embryos formed by cloning from adult cells often <u>don't develop normally</u>.

5) Cloning is also a <u>new</u> science and it might have consequences that we're <u>not yet aware of</u>. At the moment it's also <u>difficult</u>, <u>time-consuming</u> and <u>expensive</u>.

Paper 2

Revision Summary for Section 9

And that's another section finished. Award yourself a gold star, relax, get a cup of tea, and take a leisurely glance through these beautiful revision summary questions. Once you've glanced at them, you'll have to answer them. And then you'll have to check your answers and go back and revise any bits you got wrong. And then do the questions again. In fact, it's not a matter of relaxing at all. More a matter of knuckling down to lots of hard work. Oops. Sorry.

1) a) How can farmers create the ideal conditions for photosynthesis inside a glasshouse?
   b) How does this help them to improve crop yield?

2) Why do farmers use artificial fertilisers?

3) Describe how biological control reduces pest numbers.

4) Give one advantage and one disadvantage of using biological control instead of pesticides.

5) Describe the process of making yoghurt. Don't forget to name the bacteria involved.

6) Draw and label a diagram of a fermenter.

7) List the conditions that have to be controlled in a fermenter.

8) Describe the main stages in brewing beer.

9) Describe an experiment to measure carbon dioxide production by yeast during anaerobic respiration.

10) What is selective breeding?

11) Give three examples of the use of selective breeding.

12) Describe how fish farms reduce the following:
    a) disease,
    b) interspecific predation,
    c) intraspecific predation.

13) How can the water quality in fish farms be controlled?

14) Describe the function of:
    a) a restriction enzyme,
    b) a ligase.

15) What is a vector?

16) Give an account of the important stages of genetically engineering a bacterium
    to produce the human insulin gene.

17) What is a transgenic organism?

18) Describe one way plants can be genetically modified to help improve food production.

19) Give an advantage of producing cloned plants.

20) Describe the process of micropropagation.

21) Describe the process of cloning an animal from an adult cell (e.g. cloning a sheep).

22) Describe the advantages and disadvantages of cloning transgenic animals.

Experimental Know-How

Real scientists need to know how to plan and carry out scientific experiments. Unluckily for you, those pesky examiners think you should be able to do the same — that's why up to 25% of your marks will come from questions that test your experimental know-how. Don't worry though — that's what this section's all about.

You Might Get Asked Questions on Reliability and Validity

1) RELIABLE results come from experiments that give the same data:

> - each time the experiment is repeated (by you),
> - each time the experiment is reproduced by other scientists.

2) VALID results are both reliable AND come from experiments that were designed to be a fair test.

In the exam, you could be asked to suggest ways to improve the reliability or validity of some experimental results. If so, there are a couple of things to think about:

① Controlling Variables Improves Validity

1) A variable is something that has the potential to change, e.g. temperature.
In a lab experiment you usually change one variable and measure how it affects another variable.

> EXAMPLE: you might change only the temperature of an enzyme-controlled reaction and measure how it affects the rate of reaction.

2) To make it a fair test, everything else that could affect the results should stay the same — otherwise you can't tell if the thing you're changing is causing the results or not.

> EXAMPLE continued: you need to keep the pH the same, otherwise you won't know if any change in the rate of reaction is caused by the change in temperature, or the change in pH.

3) The variable you CHANGE is called the INDEPENDENT variable.
4) The variable you MEASURE is called the DEPENDENT variable.
5) The variables that you KEEP THE SAME are called CONTROL variables.

> EXAMPLE continued:
> Independent variable = temperature
> Dependent variable = rate of reaction
> Control variables = pH, volume of reactants, concentration of reactants etc.

6) Because you can't always control all the variables, you often need to use a CONTROL EXPERIMENT — an experiment that's kept under the same conditions as the rest of the investigation, but doesn't have anything done to it. This is so that you can see what happens when you don't change anything at all.

② Carrying Out Repeats Improves Reliability

1) To improve reliability you need to repeat any measurements you make and calculate the mean (average).
2) You need to repeat each measurement at least three times.

Reliable results — they won't ever forget your birthday...

A typical exam question might describe an experiment, then ask you to suggest what variables need to be controlled. Don't panic, just use your scientific knowledge and a bit of common sense, e.g. if the experiment involves enzymes, you know that they're affected by things like temperature and pH, so these variables need to be kept constant (providing you're not actually measuring one of them). You might also need to say how you'd control the variables, e.g. the temperature of a test tube-based reaction could be controlled using a water bath.

Experimental Know-How

Thought you knew <u>everything</u> there was to know about experiments? <u>Think again</u> my friend...

You Might Have to Suggest Ways to Make an Experiment Safer

1) It's important that experiments are safe. If you're asked to suggest ways to make an experiment safer, you'll first need to identify what the <u>potential hazards</u> might be. Hazards include things like:

Hmm... Where did my bacteria sample go?

- <u>Microorganisms</u>, e.g. some bacteria can make you ill.
- <u>Chemicals</u>, e.g. sulfuric acid can burn your skin and alcohols catch fire easily.
- <u>Fire</u>, e.g. an unattended Bunsen burner is a fire hazard.
- <u>Electricity</u>, e.g. faulty electrical equipment could give you a shock.

2) Then you'll need to suggest ways of <u>reducing</u> the <u>risks</u> involved with the hazard, e.g.

- If you're working with <u>sulfuric acid</u>, always wear gloves and safety goggles. This will reduce the risk of the acid coming into contact with your skin and eyes.
- If you're using a <u>Bunsen burner</u>, stand it on a heat proof mat. This will reduce the risk of starting a fire.

You Could be Asked About Accuracy...

1) It's important that results are <u>ACCURATE</u>. Really accurate results are those that are <u>really close</u> to the <u>true answer</u>.

2) The accuracy of your results usually depends on your <u>method</u>.

E.g. say you wanted to measure the <u>rate</u> of an <u>enzyme-controlled reaction</u> that releases a <u>gas</u> as a product. The rate of the reaction would be the <u>amount of gas produced per unit time</u>. You could <u>estimate</u> how much gas is produced by <u>counting</u> the number of <u>bubbles</u> that are released. But the bubbles could be <u>different sizes</u>, and if they're produced really quickly you might <u>miss some</u> when counting. It would be more accurate to <u>collect the gas</u> (e.g. in a gas cylinder) and <u>measure</u> its <u>volume</u>.

3) To make sure your results are as <u>accurate</u> as possible, you also need to make sure you're measuring the <u>right thing</u> and that you <u>don't miss anything</u> that should be included in the measurements.

E.g. if you want to know the <u>length</u> of a <u>potato chip</u>, you need to <u>start measuring</u> from '<u>0 cm</u>' on the ruler, <u>not</u> the <u>very end</u> of the ruler (or your measurement will be a few mm too short).

...And Precision

1) Results also need to be <u>PRECISE</u>. Precise results are those taken using <u>sensitive instruments</u> that measure in <u>small increments</u>, e.g. using a ruler with a millimetre scale gives more precise data than using a ruler with a scale in centimetres.

2) By recording your results to a <u>greater number</u> of <u>decimal places</u>, you'll increase their precision, e.g.

In some exam questions, you'll be told how precise to be in your answer. So if you're told to give an answer to 2 decimal places, make sure you do or you could lose marks.

Repeat	Data set 1	Data set 2
1	12	11.98
2	14	14.00
3	13	13.01

The results in data set 2 are more precise than those in data set 1.

Safety first — goggles on before you read this book...

It may interest you to know that you won't just have to write about other people's experiments in the exam. Sometimes you'll be asked to <u>describe</u> how you'd carry out your <u>own experiment</u> and all this stuff about reliability and what not will apply then too. Ah. From the look on your face, I'm guessing it didn't interest you to know that.

Drawing Graphs and Interpreting Results

If you're presented with some results from an experiment you've got to know <u>what to do with them</u>.

You Should Be Able to Identify Anomalous Results

1) Most results vary a bit, but any that are <u>totally different</u> are called <u>anomalous results</u>.

2) They're <u>caused</u> by <u>human errors</u>, e.g. by a mistake made when measuring or by not setting up a piece of equipment properly.

3) You could be asked to <u>identify</u> an anomalous result in the exam and suggest what <u>caused</u> it — just look for a result that <u>doesn't fit in</u> with the rest (e.g. it's <u>too high</u> or <u>too low</u>) then try to figure out what could have <u>gone wrong</u> with the experiment to have caused it.

4) If you're calculating an <u>average</u>, you can <u>ignore</u> any anomalous results.

You Need to Be Able to Draw Graphs...

In the exam, you might be asked to draw a <u>graph</u> or <u>bar chart</u> from a set of results.
If you're not told which one to go for, here's how you decide:

1) If the independent variable is <u>categoric</u> (comes in distinct categories, e.g. blood types, metals) you should use a <u>bar chart</u> to display the data.

2) If the independent variable is <u>continuous</u> (can take any value within a range, e.g. length, volume, time) you should use a <u>line graph</u> to display the data.

Here are a few useful tips for <u>drawing line graphs</u>:

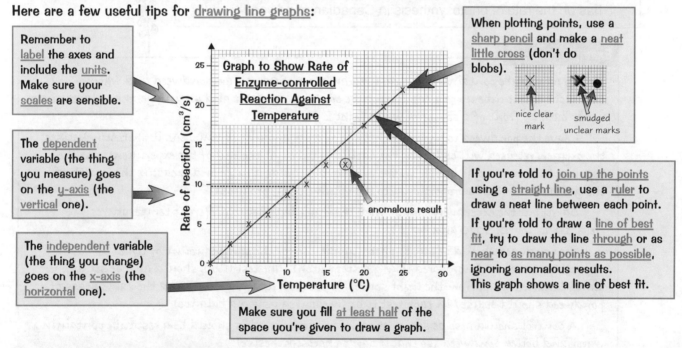

Remember to <u>label</u> the axes and include the <u>units</u>. Make sure your <u>scales</u> are sensible.

The <u>dependent</u> variable (the thing you measure) goes on the <u>y-axis</u> (the <u>vertical</u> one).

The <u>independent</u> variable (the thing you change) goes on the <u>x-axis</u> (the <u>horizontal</u> one).

When plotting points, use a <u>sharp pencil</u> and make a <u>neat little cross</u> (don't do blobs).

nice clear mark

smudged unclear marks

If you're told to <u>join up the points</u> using a <u>straight line</u>, use a <u>ruler</u> to draw a neat line between each point.

If you're told to draw a <u>line of best fit</u>, try to draw the line <u>through</u> or as <u>near</u> to <u>as many points as possible</u>, ignoring anomalous results. This graph shows a line of best fit.

Make sure you fill <u>at least half</u> of the space you're given to draw a graph.

Graph to Show Rate of Enzyme-controlled Reaction Against Temperature

anomalous result

...And Interpret Them

1) A graph is used to show the <u>relationship</u> between two variables — you need to be able to look at a graph and <u>describe</u> this relationship. For example, the graph above shows that as <u>temperature increases</u>, <u>so does rate of reaction</u>.

2) You also need to be able to <u>read information</u> off a graph. In this example, if you wanted to know what the rate of reaction was at <u>11 °C</u>, you'd draw a <u>vertical line up</u> from the x-axis at 11 °C and a <u>horizontal line across</u> to the y-axis. This would tell you that the rate of reaction at 11 °C was around <u>9.7 cm³/s</u>.

As rate of revision increases, so does boredom...

It's not just graphs you'll have to deal with in the exam, it's <u>tables</u> too. For example, you might be asked to describe the results in a table or pick out an anomalous result. You'll also be expected to do a bit of <u>basic maths</u>, like <u>calculating</u> a <u>mean</u> (add everything together and divide by the total number of values) or a <u>percentage</u>.

Planning Experiments and Evaluating Conclusions

In the exam, you could be asked to plan or describe how you'd carry out an experiment. The experiment might be one you've already come across (easy) or (gasp) you might be asked to come up with an experiment of your own to test something. I know. Examiners are harsh. It's not as bad as it sounds though. You might also be asked to say what you think of someone else's conclusion.

You Need to Be Able to Plan a Good Experiment

Here are some general tips on what to include when planning an experiment:

1) Say what you're measuring (i.e. what the dependent variable is going to be).

2) Say what you're changing (i.e. what the independent variable is going to be) and describe how you're going to change it.

3) Describe the method and the apparatus you'd use (e.g. to measure the variables).

4) Describe what variables you're keeping constant — and how you're going to do it.

5) Say that you need to repeat the experiment three times, to make the results more reliable.

6) Say whether you're using a control or not.

Here's an idea of the sort of thing you might be asked in the exam and what you might write as an answer...

Exam-style Question:

1 Describe an investigation to find out what effect temperature has on the rate of photosynthesis in Canadian pondweed. (6)

Example Answer:

Set up a test tube containing a measured amount of Canadian pondweed and water. Connect the test tube up to a capillary tube containing water and a syringe, then place it in a water bath in front of a source of white light.

Leave the pondweed to photosynthesise for a set amount of time. As it photosynthesises, the oxygen released will collect in the capillary tube. At the end of the experiment, use the syringe to draw the gas bubble in the tube up alongside a ruler and measure the length of the gas bubble. This is proportional to the volume of O_2 produced.

Carry out the experiment again with the water bath set to different temperatures (e.g. 10 °C, 20 °C, 30 °C and 40 °C).

The pondweed should be left to photosynthesise for the same amount of time at each temperature (monitored using a stopwatch). The test tubes should also be set up the same distance away from the light source (measured using a ruler) and the same mass of pondweed should be used in each test tube (measured using a balance).

A control should also be set up at each temperature. This should be a test tube containing water and boiled pondweed (so that it can't photosynthesise).

Repeat the experiment three times at each temperature and use the results to find an average rate of photosynthesis at each temperature. This will make the results more reliable.

You Could Be Asked to Evaluate a Conclusion

In the exam, you could be given an experimental conclusion and asked to evaluate it. This just means saying whether or not you think evidence from the experiment supports the conclusion — and why.

Plan your way to exam success...

The number of marks available for a question like this will vary, but it'll usually be around five or six. This means you'll have to write an extended answer. Think about what you're going to say beforehand and in what order — that way you're less likely to forget something important. Like what it is you're actually measuring, say.

The Perfect Cup of Tea

The making and drinking of tea are important <u>life skills</u>. It's not something that will crop up in the exam, but it is something that will make your <u>revision</u> much <u>easier</u>. So here's a guide to making the <u>perfect cuppa</u>...

1) Choose the <u>Right Mug</u>

A good mug is an <u>essential</u> part of the tea drinking experience, but choosing the <u>right vessel</u> for your tea can be tricky. Here's a guide to choosing your mug:

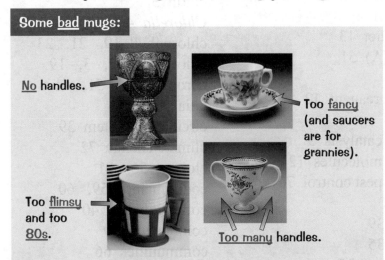

Some <u>bad</u> mugs:

<u>No</u> handles.

Too <u>fancy</u> (and saucers are for grannies).

Too <u>flimsy</u> and too <u>80s</u>.

<u>Too many</u> handles.

The <u>perfect</u> mug:

Holds just the <u>right amount</u> of tea.

Wide enough to <u>dunk a biscuit</u>.

Has a <u>design</u> that <u>complements</u> your <u>personality</u> (yes, I'm a bit hippy).

Nice, <u>easy to hold</u> handle.

2) Get Some <u>Water</u> and Boil It

For a really <u>great brew</u> follow these easy <u>step-by-step</u> instructions:

1) First, pour some <u>water</u> into a <u>kettle</u> and switch it <u>on</u>. (Check it's switched on at the wall too.)

2) Let the kettle <u>boil</u>. While you're waiting, see what's on **TV** later and check your belly button for fluff. Oh, and put a <u>tea bag</u> in a <u>mug</u>.

3) Once the kettle has boiled, <u>pour</u> the water into the mug.

4) <u>Mash</u> the tea bag about a bit with a spoon. <u>Remove</u> the tea bag.

5) Add a splash of <u>milk</u> (and a lump of <u>sugar</u> or two if you're feeling naughty).

Top tea tip no. 23: why not ask your mum if she wants a cup too?

Note: some people may tell you to add the milk <u>before</u> the tea. Scientists have recently confirmed that this is <u>nonsense</u>.

3) Sit Back <u>and</u> Relax

Now this is important — once you've <u>made</u> your cuppa:

1) Have a quick rummage in the kitchen cupboards for a <u>cheeky biscuit</u>. (Custard creams are best — steer clear of any ginger biscuits — they're evil.)

2) Find your favourite <u>armchair/beanbag</u>. Move the <u>cat</u>.

3) Sit back and <u>enjoy</u> your mug of tea. You've <u>earned it</u>.

Phew — time for a brew I reckon...

It's best to <u>ignore</u> what other people say about making cups of tea and follow this method. Trust me, this is the most <u>definitive</u> and <u>effective</u> method. If you don't do it this way, you'll have a <u>shoddy drinking experience</u>. There, you've been warned. Now go and get the kettle on. Mine's milk and two sugars...

Index

Index

Index

Index

Index and Answers

Answers

Revision Summary for Section 1 (page 11)

17) a) pH 1.65
          (accept answers between 1.6 and 1.7)

Revision Summary for Section 3 (page 27)

4) a) 40 units
    b) temperature and light

Revision Summary for Section 5 (page 42)

11) Vessel C) is a vein.

     You can tell this because it has a large
     lumen and thin walls. A) is a capillary and
     is far too small to be a vein. B) is an artery
     — the walls are too thick to be a vein and
     the lumen isn't large enough.

Revision Summary for Section 7 (page 65)

21)

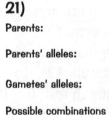
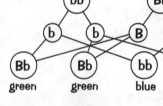

Parents:	blue eyes	green eyes
Parents' alleles:	bb	Bb
Gametes' alleles:	b b	B b
Possible combinations of alleles in offspring:	Bb Bb	bb bb
	green green	blue blue

Probability of the couple having a blue-
eyed child is 50%/1 in 2. Phenotypic ratio
is blue:green, 1:1.